OPTICS AND
OPTICAL INSTRUMENTS

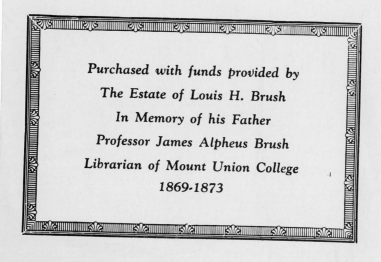

OPTICS AND OPTICAL INSTRUMENTS

An Introduction with Special Reference
to Practical Applications

(Formerly Titled: Practical Optics)

BY B. K. JOHNSON

ASSISTANT PROFESSOR AT THE IMPERIAL
COLLEGE OF SCIENCE AND TECHNOLOGY,
SOUTH KENSINGTON, LONDON

RECOGNIZED LECTURER
OF THE UNIVERSITY OF LONDON

DOVER PUBLICATIONS, INC.
NEW YORK NEW YORK

Published in the United Kingdom by Constable
and Company Limited, 10 Orange Street,
London W.C. 2.

This new Dover edition, first published in 1960,
is an unabridged and unaltered republication of
the second edition published in 1947 under the
former title: *Practical Optics*.

Library of Congress Catalog Card Number: 60-3186

Manufactured in the United States of America

Dover Publications, Inc.
180 Varick Street
New York 14, N.Y.

FOREWORD TO DOVER EDITION

THIS book is intended to convey information concerning the practical application of optical principles. In recent years optical instruments and optical components have been used increasingly in scientific and industrial work, and it has become evident that there are still many who may not be familiar with optical technique. It was felt, therefore, that if the latter was explained in practical and concise form, this might prove helpful both to the student and to the industrial physicist.

It is a well-known truism that theory should be supported by experimental verification, and to this end experiments and optical working models are set out in some detail in these pages, so as to enable the theoretical principles to be grasped and also to enable one to understand better the action of the lenses and prisms, etc., often hidden by the external tubes or casings of the finished instrument.

Whilst the book is of a practical nature, sufficient theory is given to enable the experimental illustrations to be carried out intelligently.

Since the book was first printed in 1947, two additional chapters have been introduced, one dealing with the human eye and one concerned with optical projection apparatus.

It is hoped that the section on optical glass and its working will prove of value and lead to a fuller appreciation of the art and skill required in producing high quality optical components.

It was felt that the practical application of fundamental optical principles to almost every branch of science and industry is now so far-reaching that the existence of the third edition of this book would be justified.

For those who have to teach these principles, for the users of optical instruments, and for those who do research work, it is hoped that these pages may contribute in some small way to their work.

B.K.J.

Imperial College, London, 1960.

CONTENTS

OPTICS AND
OPTICAL INSTRUMENTS

PRACTICAL OPTICS

CHAPTER I

REFLECTION AND REFRACTION OF LIGHT

Ray-projector.

Some of the more introductory principles of reflection and refraction may be conveniently illustrated and verified by utilizing narrow' beams of light sent out by a miniature projection lantern which can be moved about on a drawing board. Such a method whereby " rays " of light can be seen on the white paper being reflected to or from mirrors or through refracting systems, brings out the principles in vivid fashion; and a more lasting impression is made in the student's mind than by doing such experiments by other methods.

Fig. 1.
Ray Projector for use on a Drawing Board.

The ray-projector, as it will be called, consists of a 12-volt, 36-watt, motor-car lamp bulb (with line filament) situated at the focus of a cylindrical lens rectangular in form (about $3\frac{1}{2}''/1\frac{1}{2}''$), with provision for interposing metal plates (having slots about $\frac{1}{16}''$ wide) in front of the lens, the whole being suitably housed in order to screen off stray light. The device is illustrated in Fig. 1, which will be found self-explanatory.

1

Fig. 2 shows some of the accessories which may be used with the ray-projector in order to carry out the experiments which follow.

Laws of Reflection.

In order to prove experimentally that the angles of incidence and reflection are equal for rays meeting a reflecting surface, a method similar to that depicted in Fig. 3, may be employed. Draw a semi-circle of six inches radius and mark off intervals of ten-degree angles

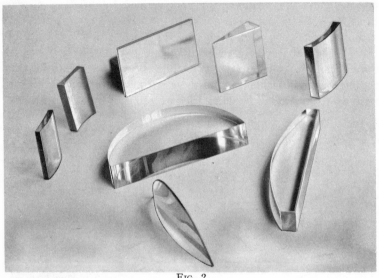

FIG. 2.
Accessories for carrying out " Ray " Experiments.

round a semi-circle of the circumference. Place a piece of plain mirror (preferably surface silvered) cemented to a wooden block along the diameter of the semi-circle with its face perpendicular to the drawing paper. Place the ray-projector round the circumference of the circle so that a narrow beam is projected along the 30 degree line; observe the angle at which the beam is reflected from the mirror, which should of course agree with the angle of incidence, namely, 30 degrees. Repeat the experiment for a number of different angles of incidence.

Angular Magnification by a Mirror.

Re-position the ray-projector so that the beam makes an angle of incidence and reflection of 30 degrees as before. Now rotate the mirror through 20 degrees until its face coincides with the line marked 70 on the left of the diagram. Find the new direction of the reflected ray.

Observe that the reflected ray moves through *twice* the angle moved by the mirror. In a sense this may be termed a form of magnification, inasmuch as the method facilitates the determination of small angular movements by doubling the effect through the medium of an attached mirror to the moving part; for example, in measuring the rotation of a galvanometer suspension.

Image in a Plane Mirror is same distance behind Mirror as Object is in Front.

Replace the silvered mirror by a piece of plane glass (supported at its end) along the line 90,90. Insert a pin at some such point as A.

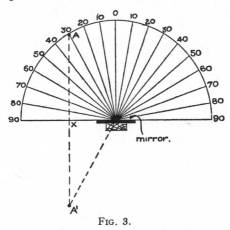

FIG. 3.

Looking into the plane glass mirror place a second pin at A′ so that the latter appears to coincide with A. Join AA′. Measure AX and A′X. Note that these distances are equal and that AA′ is perpendicular to the line 90,90.

Reflection by two Mirrors Inclined at a Finite Angle.

A ray or beam of light reflected in two mirrors in succession will be deviated through an angle equal to twice the exterior angle between the mirrors.

Set up two mirrors perpendicular to the drawing paper, but with their edges adjacent to one another. (See Fig. 4.) Arrange them so that the angle between the mirrors is 135 degrees. Draw a line AB so that it makes an angle of incidence of 80 degrees with the normal to the first mirror. Direct the ray-projector so that a narrow beam travels along AB, and mark the direction CD on the paper as it emerges from the second mirror. Remove the mirrors, produce the line AB to P and produce CD until it intersects ABP in the point O.

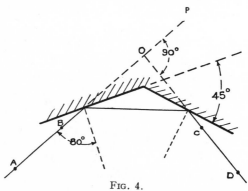

FIG. 4.

Measure the angle POD with a protractor and compare it with the exterior angle between the two mirrors, namely, 45 degrees. The angle POD should be twice the latter.

Mirrors at 90 degrees.

Arrange the mirrors to be at right angles to one another, and direct a beam from the ray-projector so that it meets one of the mirrors at any angle of incidence. Note that the beam reflected from the second mirror is deviated through 180 degrees and returns parallel to the incidence beam. Observe that the reflected beam maintains a constant deviation, no matter at what angle the incident beam strikes the first mirror.

Mirrors at 45 degrees.

Arrange the two mirrors to be inclined at 45 degrees (i.e., exterior angle 135 degrees) and direct the ray-projector towards one of the mirrors. Note that the beam emerges from the second mirror after having been deviated through 270 degrees and therefore at right angles to the incident beam. Move the ray-projector round a little so that the beam strikes the first mirror at a different angle of incidence and observe that the deviation always remains constant. This illustrates the principle of the " optical square " as used in surveying, and the pentagonal prism as used in range-finders. If one of the latter prisms

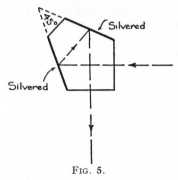

FIG. 5.

is available (see Fig. 5 and Fig. 10) this should be placed in the incident beam and rotated.

Reversals caused by Reflecting Systems.

Place a three slit diaphragm in front of the condenser of the ray-projector instead of the single slit and then arrange two mirrors as indicated in Fig. 6. Mark on the paper the incident rays 1, 2 and 3,

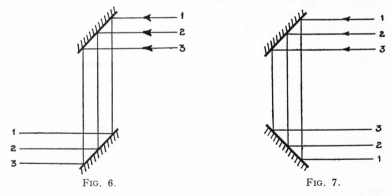

FIG. 6.   FIG. 7.

and observe that they emerge from the second mirror un-reversed. The simple periscope and the sextant are examples of the instruments which utilize this principle.

Binocular Prism.

Place the second mirror so that it opposes the first. (See Fig. 7.) Note that in the plane of the paper the rays are reversed.

If instead of the three slit diaphragm a transparent letter R mounted on an opaque background be placed in front of the condenser of the ray-projector and a four inch focus lens arranged so as to produce an image of the letter R on a ground glass screen mounted on the drawing paper, it will be found possible to observe reversals " up and down " as well as " right and left."

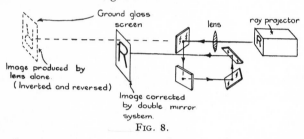

FIG. 8.

In this connection, by mounting two other mirrors, as in Fig. 8, on wooden supports and placing them so that the line joining the centres of the two mirrors is perpendicular to the plane of the paper, and then using the ground glass screen as indicated, the double reversal will be clearly seen. This illustrates the way in which two right-angled prisms are employed in the prismatic binocular, known as the Porro prism system. It should be remembered that in telescope lens systems the object glass gives an image which is reversed " up and down " and " right and left," and in many cases this has to be compensated for by some form of reflecting system.

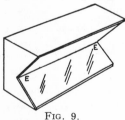

FIG. 9.

Roof-Edge principle.

Fig. 9 shows two plane mirrors mounted in a suitable wooden base so that they adjoin one another along the so-called roof edge EE.

If the beam from the illuminated letter R is allowed to fall on the two mirrors resting on the drawing board so that the roof edge EE is parallel to the drawing board, but at 45 degrees to the incident light and the ground glass screen arranged to receive the reflected image, it will be seen that the latter is both reversed and inverted. This principle is of considerable importance, for it is adopted in making many forms of prisms which are employed in telescope systems required to give an erect image of the object being observed. Some types of roof prisms are illustrated in Fig. 10.

FIG. 10.

Tetrahedron.	Erecting Prism. (One direction only)	Three
Lehman Prism.	Pentagonal Prism.	Forms of
	Binocular Prism. (Porro)	Roof Prism.

Reflection by Roof Mirrors combined with one or more Plane Mirrors.

Set up the illuminated letter R and the roof mirrors as in the foregoing experiment, and then reflect the beam on to the ground glass screen by means of one plane mirror. Observe that one reversal is now corrected, but if a second plane mirror is placed as indicated in Fig. 11, the reversal and inversion remains complete. This is the principle of the periscope erecting device utilized in telescopic systems, and is due to Lehman. It is important to note that when a roof reflector is employed with plane reflectors, the number of the latter must always be *even* in order to give reversal and inversion.

One form of a Lehman prism is shown in Fig. 12 and in Fig. 10.

Number of Images in two Inclined Plane Mirrors.

This is denoted by $(360/\theta) - 1$, where θ is the angle between the mirrors. Set up two mirrors inclined at 90 degrees on a piece of

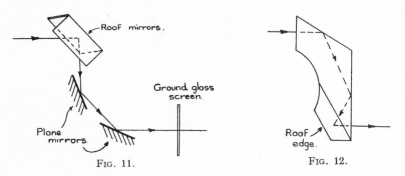

FIG. 11.   FIG. 12.

white paper. Place some object (e.g. a piece of red sealing wax about ½-in. wide) between the mirrors as shown in Fig. 13. Note that the number of images is three. Set the mirrors at some other angle, calculate and observe the number of images. When set at 60 degrees, the principle of the kaleidoscope will be illustrated.

Corner Cube or Tetrahedron.

Arrange three mirrors such that they are all at right angles to one another as in Fig. 14. If one then looks into the corner of the solid

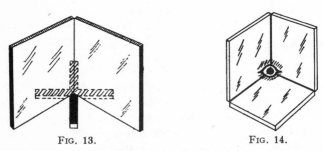

FIG. 13.   FIG. 14.

right angle, an image of the eye will be seen, and, no matter how the head is moved about, an image of the eye will always be seen right in the corner, thus showing that the incident and reflected rays travel along identical paths. A piece of glass made with three silvered faces containing a solid right angle is sometimes made and is called a tetrahedron prism. (See Fig. 10.) If a beam of light be directed towards such a prism in a darkened area, an observer will see the reflected beam only if his eye is in line with the projected beam. Therefore such devices are made use of by fixing them to the rear of motor vehicles, for example, or to the stern of ships at sea, or as road signs, so that a beam of light striking them makes them appear brightly illuminated to the driver of following vehicles.

Concave and Convex Mirrors.

By directing the ray-projector (with seven slits in front of the condenser) towards a cylindrical concave mirror of about 6in. radius, the rays will be seen coming to a focus (see Fig. 15). The latter

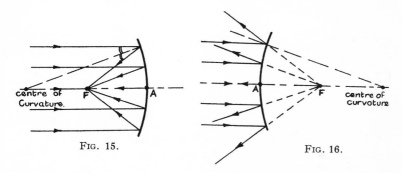

Fig. 15.　　　　　Fig. 16.

can be marked on the paper and a line should also be drawn round the inner edge of the mirror. Remove the mirror and find its radius of curvature by trial with a pair of compasses. Measure the distance AF between the focus and the mirror and show that this is equal to half the radius.

If the mirror is made from a curved metal strip and polished on both sides, it may be reversed and used as a convex mirror. As before, send on to this a set of parallel rays and note that they now diverge after meeting the reflecting surface. (See Fig. 16.) Mark their directions on the drawing paper, also the circumference of the mirror. Remove the latter and produce back the reflected rays until they meet the axis at F. Then AF will be the focus of the mirror, which should again be equal to half the radius.

Laws of Refraction.

This experiment illustrates in simple form the relation N. sin $i =$ N'. sin r where i and r are the angles of incidence and refraction for a ray of light passing from a medium of refractive index N to one of refractive index N'.

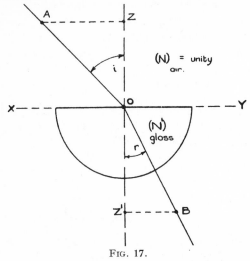

FIG. 17.

A semi-circular glass block (Fig. 17) is laid on the drawing paper so that the flat polished surface coincides with the pencil line XY. At the centre point O, draw a line AO, making an angle of (say 45 degrees) with the normal OZ. Direct the ray-projector so that the narrow beam from a single slit passes along the direction AO. (It may be advisable to screen off all but an eighth of an inch of the surface at O.) Where the refracted ray emerges from the block, mark some position B in the illuminated beam. Remove the glass block, join BO. Along AO measure off a distance OA equal in length to OB and drop perpendiculars AZ and BZ' from the points A and B to the normal ZZ'. The length AZ divided by BZ' will then give the refractive index of the glass block N'.

Repeat the experiment for other values of the angle i and note in each case that the relation N. sin $i =$ N' sin r is a constant.

Critical Angle and Total Internal Reflection.

In the special case of the law of refraction when i becomes 90 degrees, both its sine and the refractive index (N) of air being equal to unity, the equation then assumes the form $\sin r = \dfrac{1}{N'}$. This particular value for the angle r is called the critical angle for the glass concerned with respect to air. To measure this experimentally, direct a single narrow beam from the ray-projector in the direction BO into the semi-circular glass block (Fig. 17.) Having marked the position O on the drawing paper, rotate the block about this point (making the angle BOZ′ gradually larger) until the emergent ray OA becomes parallel to the flat surface of the block (i.e., grazing emergence.) This will be found to be quite a sensitive setting. Measure the angle BOZ′, which will be the critical angle, and from this the refractive index of the glass may be obtained.

If one continues to rotate the block, it will be noticed that the ray is internally reflected and emerges with the angle of reflection equal to the angle of incidence.

The above experiment may be repeated with a block of higher refractive index material, such as a dense flint glass or, alternatively, with a semi-circular glass trough containing a liquid such as carbon disulphide.

Refraction through a Prism.

Direct a single ray along the drawing paper and mark this direction on the latter. Insert a small angled prism (e.g., between 10 and 15 degrees) in the beam and mark the direction of the refracted ray. Remove the prism, join the lines and produce them to intersect one another; measure the deviation (D) thus produced, also the angle of the prism (A) by means of a protractor. Observe that for small angled prisms $D = (N-1)\ A$ where N is the refractive index of the prism which may be taken as 1·520.

Secondly, insert a prism (preferably of dense flint glass) having a sixty degree angle—it may be necessary to place a green filter in front of the single slit of the ray-projector in order to eliminate the other spectrum colours. Rotate the prism about an axis parallel to the refracting edge and observe that the deviation reaches a minimum and then increases again, even though a continued rotation is given to the prism. Determine the position of the prism, which gives minimum deviation and make pencil lines along the edges of the prism faces. Also, make two marks on the drawing paper in the paths of the incident and refracted rays, join these respective points and draw a line so that they meet the lines indicating the prism faces. At these intersections draw normals to the prism faces and measure the angles of incidence and emergence, also the angle of deviation, and note that when the latter has a minimum value, the angles of incidence and emergence are equal. With the numerical values thus measured, the approximate refractive index of the prism may be obtained from

$$\frac{\sin\left(\dfrac{A + D}{2}\right)}{\sin A/2}$$

If the single slit is illuminated with white light and a screen placed in the emergent beam at some distance from the prism, a spectrum will be seen.

Action of a Lens.

Fit the ray-projector with a five-slit or seven-slit mask in front of the condenser so that a number of parallel rays are seen traversing the drawing paper. In the path of these rays interpose a plano-convex slab lens (the curved surface being about 10 cm. radius) and arrange the central ray to pass along the axis of the lens undeviated. Observe the way in which the other rays are refracted and made to intersect on the axis at approximately the same point. This point is called the focus of the lens and its distance from the latter is known as the focal length, namely, 20 cm.

Similarly, a concave slab lens may be rested on the drawing paper in the path of the parallel rays. It will be noted that the rays diverge after passing through the lens; if the direction of these are marked and produced back until they intersect on the axial ray (after the lens has been removed) the distance between this intersection point and the lens will give the focal length.

Lens Aberrations.

If the semi-circular glass block be used as a lens and placed with the convex surface towards the incident parallel rays, the spherical aberration will be sufficiently great to enable the distance between the position at which the extreme marginal rays cross the axis and that at which the paraxial rays meet the axis to be seen clearly on the paper.

If the central rays are stopped out and only the extreme marginal rays are allowed to pass through the lens, the chromatic aberration may be observed by first putting a red and then a blue filter in front of the ray-projector.

By returning to the set-up with seven incident parallel rays, the semi-circular block (now acting as a lens) may be rotated on the paper, when it will be noticed that the rays from the marginal parts of the lens no longer intersect on the axial rays, but are displaced, illustrating the aberration known as coma.

Telescopes.

The path of rays through a telescope lens system may be clearly illustrated by means of the ray-projector. Using the 20 cm. focal-length slab lens in the path of the incident parallel rays, locate the focus and place a much shorter focus positive cylindrical slab lens (of about 4 cm. or 5 cm. focus) in some position beyond the focus of the first lens such that the rays emerge parallel after leaving the second lens.

FIG. 18.

Repeat the experiment by substituting a short focus concave lens as the eyepiece lens, but in this case it will be found necessary to place it *between* the first lens and its focus in order to render parallel the emerging rays. This experiment shows the principle of the Galilean or terrestrial telescope, whereas the former illustrates the astronomical or inverting type of telescope.

Now, alter the direction of the ray-projector so that the central ray passes through the centre of the first lens, but making an angle of, say, 5 degrees with the axis. (See Fig. 18.) The direction of the parallel rays leaving the eyepiece lens may then be marked and the angle they make with axis of the telescope measured.

This angle is that under which the final virtual image would be seen by the eye, whereas the angle under which the object would be seen directly (neglecting the length of the telescope) would be the initial 5 degrees. The former angle divided by the latter gives the magnification of the telescope.

Erecting Prism.

The combined effect of refraction and reflection is utilized in one form of erecting prism depicted in Fig. 19 and Fig. 10. The reversing effect may be beautifully shown by directing a single ray parallel to the hypotenuse of a right angled prism, first near the point A and then gradually move the ray-projector (with its single slit) across the drawing paper, keeping the incident ray parallel to the hypotenuse. It will then be noticed that the ray incident near A emerges near C, and when the incident ray is near B it emerges near D (all rays suffering refraction at faces AB and CD and total internal reflection at AD), thus producing a one-way reversal. If the incident ray is moved on beyond B, the refracted ray at the first surface is internally reflected on meeting the face CD and therefore does not emerge beyond CD; hence the effective aperture of the prism may be obtained as indicated by the line BC.

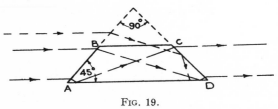

Fig. 19.

In all the foregoing experiments in refraction, should it be possible to have the glass blocks, lenses, prisms, etc., made in uranium glass or other material in which small particles are held in suspension, it is then possible to see the path of the rays *in* the glass and not merely where the rays enter and where they leave the material. Admittedly, this may seem an unnecessary luxury! But, nevertheless, the fact of seeing the rays throughout their journey conveys the effects more forcibly to the student.

Ray-Tracing Methods.

It may be necessary in certain optical problems to trace rays through such systems with greater accuracy than the ray-projector methods would allow, and, indeed, with lens systems ray-tracing methods can be distinctly useful in providing information about the design of a lens in the initial stages. The methods given in this chapter deal with two graphical methods and one strictly exact method by trigonometrical means. In order to illustrate the procedure in each case, let us take some such example as shown in Fig. 20, which may be looked upon as telephotographic lens, and trace an incident ray parallel to the axis through the lens system of the following specification:—

Lens (1)	Lens (2)
Refractive index $(N) = 1.550$	Refractive index $(N) = 1.750$
Radius $r_1 = +6.0''$	Radius $r_3 = -6.0''$
Radius $r_2 = -6.0''$	Radius $r_4 = +6.0''$
Axial thickness $= 0.70''$	Axial thickness $= 0.20''$
Diameter $= 4.0''$	Air space between lenses $= 3.0$

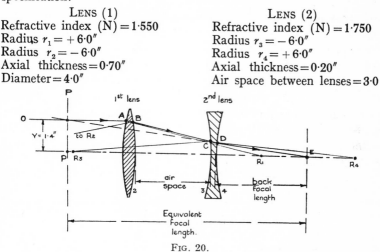

FIG. 20.

One of the better and more convenient of the graphical methods is due to Dowell* and consists of the following construction. On the drawing paper near the diagram of the lens system (already set out)

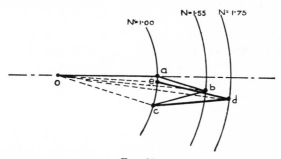

FIG. 21.

describe circles corresponding in radius to unity and the respective refractive indices of the two glass to some suitable scale. (See Fig. 21.) (Unity being taken as 10 cm. makes a convenient scale

* J. H. Dowell, *Proc. Opt. Convention* 979, 1926.

in order to give reasonable accuracy.)   From the point o draw a
line oa parallel to the incident ray OA.   At a, draw ab parallel to
the radius AR_1, cutting the N = 1·550 circle in b.   Join ob, this gives
the direction of the refracted ray in the glass of the first lens.   Draw
AB parallel to ob.

From b draw bc parallel to BR_2, cutting the unity circle in c.   Join
oc and draw BC parallel to oc.   This will be the direction of the ray
as it leaves the lens.   Then draw cd parallel to the third radius CR_3
cutting the N = 1·750 circle in d.   Draw CD parallel to od.   And
finally draw de parallel to DR_4 cutting the unity circle at e.   Join oe

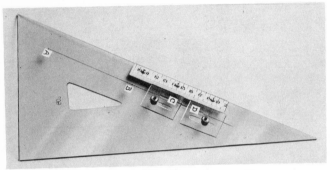

FIG. 22.
Graphical Ray Plotter.

and make DE parallel to this.   The point E will represent the focal
plane of the lens system, and if ED be projected back so that it intersects the initial parallel ray, the dotted line PP will give the position
of one of the principal planes of the system and the length PE is
known as the equivalent focal length.

B.K. Ray-plotter.

The second graphical method for ray-tracing consists in using a
ray-plotter*, an idea suggested by the writer and illustrated in Fig. 22.
This device has the advantage that no auxiliary constructional
diagram on the paper is required, as in the foregoing method.   The
ray-plotter consists of a sixty degree set square made in some transparent material on which is arranged a special scale calibrated in
terms of refractive indices ranging from 1·0 to 2·0 (i.e., covering
most transparent materials).

Manufactured by Messrs. Wray Ltd. (Optical Works), Bromley, Kent.

On a line parallel to the hypotenuse edge, small holes are situated at A and B. These holes are spaced at a distance equal to unity corresponding to some suitable scale. (In this case 10 cm.) Further along are two adjustable slides with other holes C and D and corresponding index lines reading off the main scale. If the instrument were to be used for tracing from air to glass or from glass to air, only one adjustable slide would be necessary; but by having two variable slides it is possible to utilize the plotter for tracing from one glass to another with no intervening air space, and, consequently, the device is of universal use for all problems connected with graphical ray-tracing in optics.

The Instrument in Use.

Procedure when tracing from air (refractive index 1·0) to glass (refractive index 1·52).

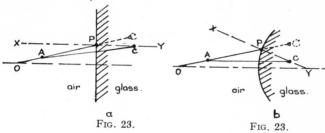

a
FIG. 23.

b
FIG. 23.

Imagine a ray OP incident at the surface at P (Fig. 23 a and b) XY are normals to the surface at P. Place the ray-plotter such that the hole B coincides with P and A lies on the incident ray. Insert a pin through the hole at A (and with the adjustable scale set to read 1·520), rotate the plotter about this point until the hole C is immediately over the normal to the surface. The direction AC is now the direction of the refracted ray and by placing a ruler along one of the edges of the set square the hypotenuse edge may be brought on to the point P and the refracted ray drawn from this point.

When tracing from glass to air, the hole C is made to coincide with the point of incidence of the ray at the surface and A placed on the ray direction. As before, the plotter is rotated about the point A but now it is B which must be brought over the normal to the surface. Thus the hypotenuse edge of the set-square again gives the direction of the refracted ray and only requires sliding to the

point of incidence of the ray at the surface, when the refracted ray
may be drawn.

Procedure when tracing from one glass (e.g., refractive index=
1·750) to another (e.g., refractive index=1·520) (see Fig. 24.)

Set slide D so that it reads 1·750 and slide C to 1·520. Then place
the ray-plotter so that the hole D coincides with P and the hole A
lies on the incident ray in the medium with N=1·750. Insert a pin
at A and rotate the plotter until the hole C lies immediately over the
normal (i.e., the radius) to the surface. As before, the hypotenuse

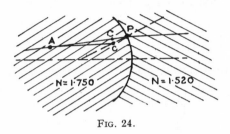

FIG. 24.

edge of the set-square will now give the direction of the refracted
ray in the medium with N=1·520 and only requires sliding to the
point of incidence P at the surface to enable the refracted ray to be
drawn.

General Rule for Use of the Instrument.

From the foregoing examples it will become clear that the general
procedure is as follows:—

When tracing rays from left to right (the usual practice) the plotter
is placed with the hole (corresponding to the refractive index of the
material to the left of the surface concerned) over the point of
incidence P and the hole A on the incident ray. With the second hole
already set on the refractive index scale corresponding to the material
to the right of the surface, rotate the instrument about the point A
until the second hole lies immediately over the normal to the surface.
Then slide the hypotenuse face of the set-square up to the point of
incidence P at the surface and draw the refracted ray.

This procedure may be continued surface by surface throughout the
entire optical system under consideration. The method proves to be
exceedingly simple and rapid when in operation.

Trigonometrical Ray-tracing.

When greater accuracy is required, one has to resort to trigono-metrical methods, and the lens system shown in Fig. 20 will be used as an example for tracing a ray trigonometrically through it in order to illustrate the methods of doing this. The five fundamental formulæ for this purpose can easily be deduced from Fig. 25 and are as follows:—

(1) $\sin I = \sin U . (L - r)/r$

(2) $\sin I' = \sin I . N/N'$

(3) $U' = U + I - I'$

(4) $L' - r = \sin I' . r/\sin U'$

(5) $L' = (L' - r) + r$

The manner in which these formulæ may be utilized for the calculation is shown on page 20, where the procedure is set out in detail. There are a few minor points of explanation which are necessary relating to the sign convention employed. Distances measured to the right of the pole of the surface A are considered

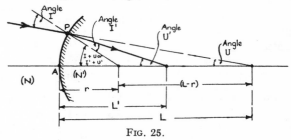

FIG. 25.

positive, whereas those to the left of A are negative. Thus for example, in the specification of the lens given on page 15 it will be noted that the surfaces 2 and 3 have radii r_2 and r_3 with a negative sign. In the case of angles, rays meeting the axis are measured from *the axis to the ray*, and if this is measured in a clockwise direction, then the angle is positive in sign; or negative if in an anti-clockwise direction. When a ray meets a surface away from the axis, such as at P (Fig. 25), then we measure from *ray to radius*, and, similarly, a clockwise direction indicates a positive angle and an anti-clockwise direction a negative angle. A further point, is that it is important to note that when taking out the logarithm of a negative quantity it is advisable to indicate this in some way; generally by putting a small letter n after the log.

	1st Surface.	2nd Surface.	3rd Surface.	4th Surface.
L	∞	15·990	1·790	4·080
$-r$		$+6\cdot000$	$+6\cdot000$	$-6\cdot000$
$(L-r)$		21·990	7·790	$-1\cdot920$
$\log \sin U$	$Y = 1\cdot40$	8·9266	9·4260	9·0627
$+\log (L-r)$		1·3422	0·8915	0·2833n
$\log(L-r)\sin U$*	0·1461	0·2688	0·3175	9·3460n
$-\log r$	0·7782	0·7782n	0·7782n	0·7782
$\log \sin I$	9·3679	9·4906n	9·5393n	8·5678n
$+\log N/N'$	9·8097	0·1903	9.7570	0·2430
$\log \sin I'$	9·1776	9·6809n	9·2963n	8·8108n
$+ \log r$	0·7782	0·7782n	0·7782n	0·7782
$\log r \sin I'$	9·9558	0·4591	0·0745	9·5890n
$-\log \sin U'$	8·9266	9·4260	9·0627	9·1554
$\log (L'-r)$	1·0292	1·0331	1·0118	0·4336n
Angle register				
U	$0-0'$	$4°-50\cdot5'$	$15°-28'$	$6°-38'$
$+I$	$13°-29\cdot5'$	$-18°-2'$	$-20°-15'$	$-2°-7'$
$U+I$	$13°-29\cdot5'$	$-13°-11\cdot5'$	$-4-47'$	$4°-31'$
$-I'$	$8°-39'$	$+28°-39\cdot5'$	$+11°-25'$	$+3°-42\cdot5'$
U'	$4°-50\cdot5'$	$15°-28'$	$6°-38'$	$8°-13\cdot5'$
$L'-r$	10·690	10·790	10·280	-2.714
$+r$	6·000	$-6\cdot000$	$-6\cdot000$	$+6\cdot000$
L'	16·690	4·790	4·280	3·286
$-$ axial thickness	0·700	3·000	0·20	————
new L	15·990	1·790	4·080	

Equivalent focal length $= \log Y -$ final $\log U' = 0\cdot1461 - 9\cdot1554 = 0\cdot9907$

Antilog $0\cdot9907 = 9\cdot788''$

Back focal length $= 3\cdot286''$

* For Parallel Light use log Y.

In the example given, only four figure logarithms and trigonometrical functions have been used, giving an angle accuracy of one minute of arc. This will be found ample for introductory work; but if serious work on optical design is contemplated, one second of arc accuracy will be called for. But this is a much bigger problem and requires considerable study. A book to recommend in this connection is *Applied Optics and Optical Design*—A. E. Conrady.

It would be desirable if the student sets himself another example as well as that worked out on page 20 in order to become familiar with the process and also carry out a graphical ray-trace. In this way an opinion may be formed as to the relative accuracy and usefulness of the two methods for any particular problem in question.

CHAPTER II

FOCAL LENGTH MEASUREMENTS

Description of Optical Bench; Optical Bench Experiments.

An optical bench of the type here described is distinctly convenient in a laboratory; its combined simplicity and comparative accuracy make it valuable for both instructional and commercial work. Fig. 26 shows the general appearance of the bench and, as will be seen, it consists of a metre steel rule supported in a vertical plane along

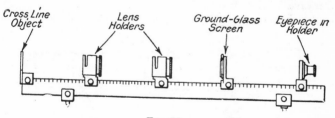

FIG. 26.

which all other necessary fittings slide. A group of these fittings is shown in Fig. 26A such as the cross-line object, ground glass screen, lens holders, mirror, etc. It will be noted that the base of all these fittings is cut away in such a manner that readings may be taken directly from the steel rule without any appreciable error being introduced. Where more accurate readings are necessary, a correction rod may be employed. The lens holders are designed to carry lenses

from any ordinary spectacle trial case, so that for experimental work
a large range of lenses may be available.

The fittings that support the steel rule in a vertical position are
also shown in Fig. 27. These are adaptable not only to the metre
rule but to shorter lengths such as a foot rule when experiments only

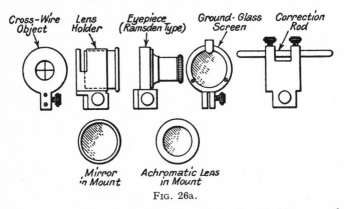

Cross-Wire Lens Eyepiece Ground-Glass Correction
Object Holder (Ramsden Type) Screen Rod

Mirror Achromatic Lens
in Mount in Mount

FIG. 26a.

involve small ranges. Scale drawings of the lens holders are shown
in Fig. 28. From these illustrations (Figs. 26 to 28) a general idea
of the optical bench may be obtained.

Measurement of the Radius of Curvature of a Concave Mirror or Concave Lens Surface.

For this experiment, a concave mirror of about 20 cm. radius

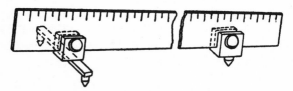

FIG. 27.

(consisting of a negative spectacle lens silvered on one of its surfaces)
may be utilised. It should be held in one of the mounts and arranged
on the optical bench together with a cross-line as object (see Fig. 29).
By illuminating the latter, the mirror may be moved to and fro until
a sharp image of the cross-line is seen back-reflected on the whitened
back surface of the cross-line mount, when the reading of this and

the mirror mount may be taken. The correction rod (of known length) should then be placed between the cross-line object and mirror, and both of them brought into position so that they make

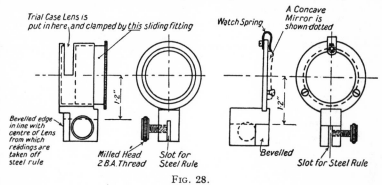

FIG. 28.

contact with the spherical ends of the rod and the readings from the optical bench scale taken once again. The difference between these two sets of readings will give the correction to be applied to the direct readings of the mirror mount and cross-line mount in order to give the correct radius of curvature of the mirror.

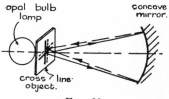

FIG. 29.

If a concave lens surface (i.e., unsilvered) is to be measured, the same procedure is adopted with the exception that the surface not under test should be covered with some material which will prevent light being reflected therefrom. (Vaseline smeared on will be found suitable for this purpose and may be easily removed without damaging the unused, polished surface of the lens.) It will be found that the back-reflected image of the cross-line from the unsilvered surface will not appear as bright as before, but amply so for satisfactory measurements.

Radius of Curvature of a Convex Mirror or a Convex Lens Surface.

Arrange the apparatus on the metre optical bench as shown in Fig. 30. O is the cross-line object at the end of the steel rule. A is a lens (held in one of the lens holder fittings) which forms an image ot the cross-wires on the ground glass screen. Determine the reading on the optical bench of the ground glass screen S when the image is sharply in focus. Interpose the convex mirror to be tested M in the position indicated and adjust its position until the image back-reflected by the mirror M is coincident with the plane of the object. The reading of the mirror is then taken, and the distance SM is the radius of curvature of the surface. For, in order that the rays

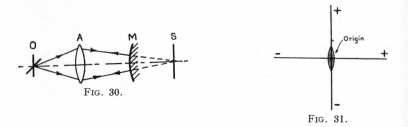

Fig. 30.

Fig. 31.

leaving O and A should retrace their paths after reflection from the mirror and form an image at O, they must strike the mirror normally; and this is only the case when the distance SM is equal to the radius of curvature of the surface. A number of independent readings should be taken for the position of M and the mean obtained.

For the determination of the radius of curvature of a convex lens surface, the same method is used, but with the back surface of the lens covered in some such material as mentioned in the previous experiment.

The Solving of " Thin " Lens and Spherical Mirror Problems.

Simple formulæ may be derived on the Gaussian principle giving the relation connecting the positions of object and image and the focal length of the lens or mirror.

In the case of spherical mirrors, the relation is

$$1/f = 2/r = 1/v + 1/u$$

and in the case of thin lenses, the relation is

$$1/f = 1/v - 1/u$$

where f is the focal length of the mirror of lens

    u is the object distance

    v is the image distance.

In order to apply these formulæ correctly, it is necessary to employ a suitable sign convention. Many and varied forms of sign convention have been used in the past, and much confusion in the mind of students has arisen on account of this. In order to clear up this matter a selected committee appointed by the Physical Society has discussed this whole subject, and its recommendations are given in the *Report on the Teaching of Geometrical Optics* (1934) (published by the Physical Society). One of their conclusions, and possibly the most convenient one, is to treat the lens or mirror as being situated at the origin of the ordinary Cartesian co-ordinates (see Fig. 31) with the proviso that " the positive direction is the initial direction of progress of the light."

Distances are then measured *from* the lens or mirror, those *against* the incident light being negative in sign and those *with* the incident light being positive.

For distances measured off the axis (such as image heights, when measuring magnification) those below the axis may be reckoned negative and those above, positive.

A further recommendation by this committee is that illustrative diagrams should as far as possible be drawn with a left-to-right progression of the light, since the sign convention of the diagram will then coincide with that of ordinary graphical work.

On this system, the focal length of a converging lens is a positive quantity and that of a diverging lens negative, so that the signs of the focal lengths agree with the signs of the powers.

This is the most generally accepted terminology in commerce at the present day, but for student's problems connected with lens and mirror equations, the system suggested in the Appendix (page 220) may be found more satisfactory.

Focal Length of a Convex Lens (Thin).

(i) Place a $+5D$ spectacle lens in one of the lens holders on the metre optical bench. Direct the optical bench at some distant bright object, for instance, a lamp placed in a long corridor—the distance should not be less than 50 yards. Place also on the bench a ground glass screen in its holder and receive an image of the distant object produced by the lens on this. The difference between the readings of the lens holder and ground glass screen holder will give the focal length of the lens. Make a number of independent settings and measure the distance in each case. See how nearly any one measurement is likely to be correct.

(ii) After having used a distant object, use an object comparatively near to the lens. This method involves the use of the formula $1/f = 1/v - 1/u$, where f is the focal length of the lens, u the distance from the lens to the object, and v the distance from the lens to the image. Due respect must be made to the use of signs when employing this formula, and it should be remembered that: distances to the left of the lens are reckoned as negative, whilst those to the right of the lens are positive. Set up the cross-line object O (Fig. 32) at one

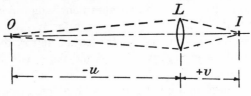

Fig. 32.

end of the optical bench and illuminate it with a lamp. Place the 5D lens L (in holder) at a distance of about 45 cm. from the object and receive an image of the cross-line on the ground glass screen. Take a number of independent readings for the position of this screen. Measure the distance u (lens to object). In this case it will have a negative value. Also measure v (lens to image) and this will have a positive sign. From these values calculate the result for f.

Move the lens to another position and repeat the experiment.

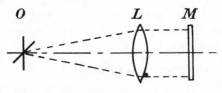

Fig. 33.

(iii) **Auto-Collimation Methods.**—It will be seen from Fig. 33 that if light diverging from the object O is rendered parallel by the lens L, reflected back by a mirror M, and again brought to a focus at O, the distance OL will be the focal length of the lens. Set up the object O at the end of the bench as before and illuminate it; place the lens about 20 cm. from the object and further along the bench place the mirror M in position. If the mirror has plane surfaces, its position relative to L is immaterial. Carefully adjust the lens holder until an image of the object is sharply focused on the whitened back of the object. (The mirror may require tilting slightly.) Measure the focal length OL. Take a number of independent readings for the position of L.

(iv) **Telescope Method.**—A small auxiliary telescope may be made up by utilising the achromatic lens and eyepiece fitting (shown in Fig. 26A) and arranging them on the right hand end of the bench at the correct separation such that a distant object is sharply focused.

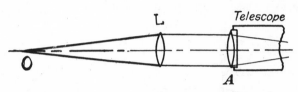

FIG. 34.

Then place the cross-line O and the lens L at the left. On observing through the telescope move L backwards and forwards until a sharply defined image of the cross-line O is seen (see Fig. 34). The distance OL will be the focal length of the lens. As before a mean value for a number of settings should be taken, and the results given by these four methods may be compared.

Focal Length of " Thin " Concave Lenses.

Set up the cross-wire object O (Fig. 35) at one end of the optical bench, and form an image of this by means of the lens A on the

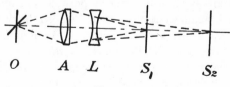

FIG. 35.

ground glass screen S_1. Place a $-3D$ lens from the trial case in one of the lens holders and insert this in the path of the convergent beam at L. Move the screen until the image is again focused, as at S_2. The image produced at S_1 by the lens A serves as the object for the negative lens, so that the distance L S_1 is u and is positive in sign, while the distance L S_2 is v and is also positive. Using the formula $1/f = 1/v - 1/u$ as before, the focal length of the negative lens may be determined. All values of readings taken from the bench should be the mean of a number of independent settings. Move the negative lens L to a fresh position and repeat the experiment.

Lens Systems—Two " Thin " Lenses in Contact.

In order to show that for two thin lenses in contact the combined power is equal to the sum of the powers of the individual lenses, the following experiment may be carried out:—

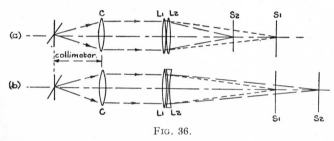

FIG. 36.

A collimator (Fig. 36a) is first set up on the optical bench, the lens C (of about 15 cm. focus) being set in its proper position by means of the " mirror method " shown in Fig. 33. In the path of the parallel beam thus produced the lens L_1 (a + 4D spectacle lens) is placed, and the image of the cross-line received on the ground glass screen S_1, the distance $L_1 S_1$ being recorded. Then, insert a lens of + 3D in another lens holder and place it on the optical bench so that the two lenses are as close together as possible and move the screen until the image is again sharply focused. Record the distance between the screen and the centre of the two lenses. By dividing this distance $L_1 S_2$ in centimetres into 100 the power of the lenses combined will be obtained, when it will be found that the two lenses in contact will give a combined power of + 7D.

Then, replace the + 3D lens by a − 1D lens (see Fig. 36b). Note that the screen S_2 has now to be moved farther from the position S_1. Record its position when the cross-line is in focus and measure the distance $L_1 S_2$. As before, obtain the power of the lens combination and note that this should now be + 3 dioptres.

This principle is the basis for the determination of the power of a lens by " matching " it with a lens of equal and opposite power. For example, if we have a lens of unknown power and we have a spectacle lens trial case at hand, a lens can be picked out from the latter which when placed in contact with the former will produce no movement of the image of an object looked at through the two lenses held and moved in front of the eye.

Two " Thin " Lenses Separated by a Known Distance.

An example demonstrating the meaning of " equivalent focal length " and " back focal length " of a lens system with an experimental verification of the two relations:—

$$f_E = \frac{f_1 f_2}{f_2 + f_1 - d} \quad \text{and } f_B = \frac{f_2 (f_1 - d)}{f_2 + f_1 - d}$$

may be shown in the following way.

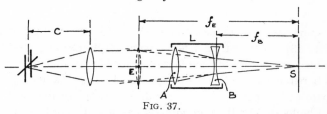

FIG. 37.

The lens system L (Fig. 37) may be made up of two trial case lenses A and B of +6D and −6D respectively, mounted in the lens holders on the optical bench and separated by a distance of 8 cm. If this be placed in the path of a parallel beam formed by means of the collimator C (having two parallel wires as object) an image of the object will be formed on the ground glass screen S, the distance BS being the **back focal length.**

To determine the **equivalent focal length,** first measure the separation of the two wires imaged on the screen S, then remove the lens system L from the bench but keep S in a fixed position. By suitable trials a single lens E may be found which will give the same sized image as that given by the lens combination L. When this has been attained, the distance ES will be the equivalent focal length. From a knowledge of the focal lengths of lenses A and B the two focal lengths f_E and f_B should be worked out from the formulæ given, and a comparison made between these values and those obtained experimentally.

Focal Length Measurement by Newton's Method.

A lens formula given by Newton states that the product of the distance of an object from the first focal point of a lens or lens system and the distance of the image from its second focal point, should be equal to the square of the focal length of the lens. Thus, referring to Fig. 38 the relation $x.x' = f^2$ is valid. Making use of this equation, the focal length of a lens system L (consisting of two similar lenses of $+4D$ power separated by 10 cm.) may be conveniently carried out.

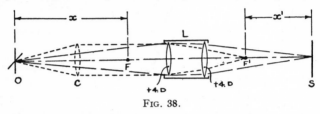

Fig. 38.

It is first necessary to find the position of the two focal points F and F' (Fig. 38). This can be done by temporarily inserting a $+5D$ lens C at the correct distance from O such that OC forms a collimator and gives a parallel beam emerging from it. Placing the lens system in the path of this parallel beam the position of one of the focal points F' can be located by the ground glass screen and recorded, for at this position an image of the cross-line will be focused. As the two lenses of this system are similar ones the position of F will be at the same distance to the left of the front lens as F' is to the right of the second lens; if desired dissimilar lenses may be used, in which case F and F' must be found individually by placing each end of the combination in turn towards the collimator.

Having, therefore, fixed the two positions of F and F', the collimating lens C is removed, and the cross-lines O moved so that the distance OF is (say) 15 cm. The screen S is then positioned until an image of the cross-line is sharply in focus and the distance F' S is measured. The square root of the product of these two distances will give the focal length of the lens system.

" Thick " Lenses and Lens Systems.

Whilst the foregoing experiments have dealt with supposed infinitely thin lenses and the application of " thin lens " formulæ, we have in many cases to deal with lenses of finite thickness and sometimes of a complex character. In these cases the thin lens formulæ no longer hold. The general principles of the Gaussian treatment of thin lens problems may, however, be applied to those of thick lenses provided we use Principal Points and Principal Planes within the lens from which the usual distances may be measured. For example, in Fig. 39 object distances would be measured from P_1 and image distances from P_2. The positions of these principal planes

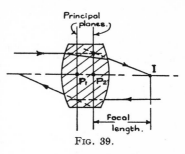

FIG. 39.

are found by the intersection point of an initial parallel ray and the corresponding finally refracted ray projected forward and backward respectively (see diagram). Thus a " thin " lens placed in the plane P_2 would have a focal length equivalent to that of the thick lens, namely, the distance P_2I. Modern requirements demand rather greater accuracy than that obtainable on the simpler form of optical bench already described, so that for more advanced work better apparatus is required. Fig. 40 shows a form of optical bench suitable for such work, and consists of a rod and bar type support one and a half metres long (divided in millimetres) on which the holders carrying the fittings slide. Some of these fittings are shown in the illustration.

Focal Length—Magnification Method.

This method can be particularly useful for measurements on compound lens systems of all kinds. The theory will be made clear from the Gaussian diagram of Fig. 41 in which an object placed at h_1 will be imaged at h_1' and the magnification thus produced will be $m_1 = h_1'/h_1 = (v_1 - f)/f$. Similarly if the object is moved nearer to the lens so that the object distance is now u_2 the image will be formed at a distance v_2 and the magnification will be $m_2 = h_2'/h_1 = (v_2 - f)/f$; by combining the two equations we get

$$f = -\frac{v_2 - v_1}{m_2 - m_1}$$

Utilising this formula in practice, a millimetre scale on glass is placed on one side of the lens at h_1 and its image is measured by means of a micrometer eyepiece situated at h_1'. The magnification may thus be obtained; this is repeated for a second position of object and image.

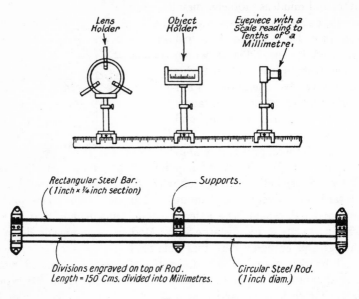

FIG. 40.

The other requirement, in order to determine the focal length is $(v_2 - v_1)$ which is the distance moved by the micrometer eyepiece

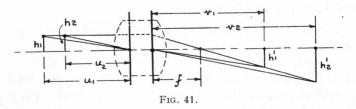

FIG. 41.

along the optical bench. It will be obvious that the formula may be derived in terms of the object distances u_1 and u_2, in which case

$$f = \frac{u_2 - u_1}{1/m_2 - 1/m_1}$$

The result given by the first formula may be checked by that given by the latter.

Negative Thick Lens.

The foregoing formulæ may be applied for the determination of the focal length of a thick negative lens or lens system. The arrangement of the experiment is that shown in Fig. 42 in which an auxiliary positive lens is used to form an image at I_1 of a glass scale. This image, which can be arranged to be of the same size as the object, serves as the object for the negative lens when it is interposed in the convergent beam. When this has been done, the

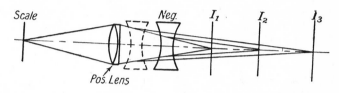

FIG. 42.

image will lie in some such plane as indicated at I_2 and can then be measured by means of the micrometer eyepiece. The ratio of the size of the image at I_2 to that at I_1 will give the magnification m_1 for use in the formula.

If the negative lens is now moved to the position shown in dotted lines, the image will move to I_3 and the magnification m_2 can be obtained. It should be noted that in determining the value $(v_2 - v_1)$ this corresponds to the distance I_2 to I_3 **plus the movement of the negative lens from its first position to its dotted position;** similarly $(u_2 - u_1)$ will be equal to the distance moved by the negative lens alone.

Foco-Collimator.

This instrument is one of the more convenient devices for focal length measurement, chiefly on account of the simplicity and rapidity of the procedure, and it is therefore ideal as a workshop tool. It consists of a collimator tube at one end of which is mounted a good quality achromatic lens of about 10 in. focus and at the other a glass plate on which are ruled two fine parallel lines A and B about 2 mm. apart (see Fig. 43) situated in the focal plane of C. These two lines subtend an angle θ at the lens C and this angle can be measured accurately by means of a theodolite. Thus, two parallel beams emerge from the collimator inclined to one another at this angle, and if the lens to be tested is placed in the path of these beams it will form images A′ and B′ in its focal plane, the separation of which can be measured by means of a micrometer eyepiece. From the geometry of the figure the triangles ABC and A′B′P are similar ones and the angle θ is common to both. The angle θ is equal to

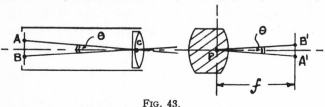

FIG. 43.

A′B′/f in circular measure, and if θ has already been determined, the focal length of the lens under test $f = A′B′ \times 1/\theta$. This latter term, namely, the reciprocal of the angle θ in radians, may be worked out as a simple multiplying factor and engraved on the collimator tube.

An additional asset to such an instrument is to have the graticule ruled with five lines each spaced at 1 mm. intervals, with factors worked out for the maximum separation and intermediate separation of the lines; so that lenses of widely different focal lengths may be accommodated for by the one instrument.

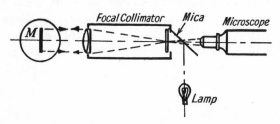

FIG. 44.

N.B.—A word may be said about the positioning of the graticule accurately at the focus of the lens C in the collimator, and indeed this remark may apply to the focusing of all collimators. The familiar " mirror method " is employed, with the refinement that the location of the lines proper and their images in the same plane is carried out by viewing the graticule with a microscope having a small depth of focus; the method is depicted in Fig. 44.

A useful modification of this instrument intended for quite short focus lenses (e.g., 2 in., 1 in. and less such as eyepieces and even microscope objectives) is shown in Fig. 45. .The collimator is attached to the stage of a microscope, and the microscope itself views the image A′B′; the latter is received on a scale situated in the eyepiece. Taking into account the magnification M of the microscope objective, the multiplying factor will then be $(1/M \times \theta)$.

Nodal Slide Method.

The nodal points of a lens are points on the axis of the system such that an incident ray passing to the first nodal point under a particular angle with the axis will leave the second nodal point under a similar angle. For example, in Fig. 46 the ray ON_1 makes an angle θ with the optical axis XY, this ray will then emerge from the nodal point N_2 under the same angle θ. When the medium on each side of the lens system is of the same refractive index, the nodal points coincide with the principal points (see Fig. 39).

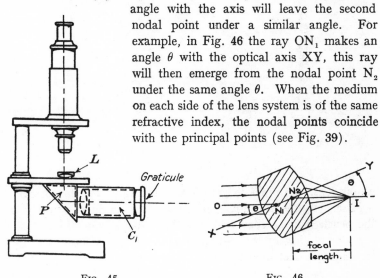

FIG. 45.   FIG. 46.

From the above principle it is easy to see that if the lens was arranged to rotate about the point N_2, the image of an object would remain stationary; and if the incident light is parallel the distance N_2I will represent the focal length of the lens. If, however, N_2 was not over the centre of rotation of the lens, then the image I would swing from side to side. This therefore gives us a method for determining the focal length of a compound lens system, for it is only necessary to have a lens mount which has rotation about a vertical axis and a means of moving the lens to and fro with respect to this axis; a collimator, and an eyepiece for observing the image. These are mounted on the optical·bench and the lens adjusted until the image at I observed with the eyepiece (or maybe a low-power microscope) appears to remain stationary, then the distance between the centre of rotation and the image plane will give the focal length

FIG. 47.

of the lens. In order to get an absolute value for this, it may be necessary to use the correction rod so that the direct readings from the bench may be converted into their true values. Fig. 47 shows a pictorial view of the optical bench set up for measurements by this method, including the nodal slide mount.

CHAPTER III

THE EYE

The human eye is the organ by means of which we obtain most of the knowledge we are concerned with in optical matters, and therefore a description of its construction is desirable. It will not be dealt with here from a physiological aspect, but more from the standpoint of an optical instrument.

Figure 48 represents a horizontal section of the human right eye. The eye is spherical in form, approximately one inch in diameter, and is surrounded with a tough, opaque outer layer known as the *sclerotic.* At the front of the eye is a more steeply curved spherical transparent layer, called the *cornea.* It is about one half of a millimetre thick, its two surfaces have an average radius of 7·2 mm., and it has a refractive index of 1·38. The space immediately behind the

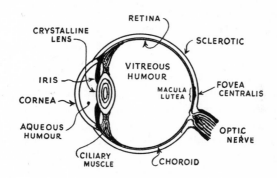

FIG. 48.

cornea is filled with a fluid, the *aqueous humour,* having a refractive index of 1·33. Following this is the *crystalline lens,* which is double convex in form and is composed of a number of transparent layers varying in refractive index from 1·41 at the centre to 1·38 in the outer layers. Under the action of the *ciliary muscle* the lens can be made to change its shape, and the power of the system is adjusted to focus images of objects at different distances on to the retina. This focusing effect is known as *accommodation,* and in normal eyes enables objects from infinity to ten inches from the eye to be seen clearly. The radii of curvature of the front and back surfaces of the crystalline lens when the eye is focused on a very distant object are about 10 mm. and 6 mm. respectively, and its thickness is approximately 3·6 mm.

The space immediately behind the crystalline lens is filled with a transparent, jelly-like medium, known as the *vitreous humour,* having a refractive index similar to that of the aqueous humour.

Directly in front of the crystalline lens is the *iris* which automatically controls the amount of light entering the eye. The circular aperture in the iris (known as the *pupil*) can be varied in diameter from about 8 mm. to 2 mm.

The inner layer adjacent to the sclerotic is called the *choroid* which contains dark pigmented cells for absorbing any light which might penetrate the sclerotic, thus preventing any such stray light from reaching the retina.

The innermost layer situated between the choroid and the vitreous humour is the *retina*. This may be looked upon as the sensitive receiving screen on which sharp images of external objects are formed. It consists of a transparent tissue covered by closely packed nerve endings from which the stimulus is conveyed to the brain, via the *optic nerve*.

A little to the right of the position at which the optic nerve enters the eye is a small area of the retina called the *macula lutea*, in the immediate centre of which is a region known as the *fovea centralis*. It is here that vision is most distinct, and is the area on which the image is arranged to fall when one is trying to resolve fine detail of an object.

Figure 49 shows a diagrammatic drawing of the human eye when treated as a centred optical system. Although the centres of the various surfaces and the pupil do not lie exactly on a common axis we may for most purposes consider the eye as a centred system. The positions of the cardinal points are indicated in the diagram; the two principal points and the two nodal points are in each case so close together that they are represented in the figure as single points P and N respectively. Some distances of importance are also shown in the diagram.

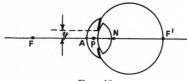

FIG. 49.

Cardinal points of the Human Eye
NF′ = 15 mm.   FA = 12.8 mm.
AN = 7.2 mm.   AP = 2.2 mm.
PF′ = 20 mm.

Emmetropia and Ametropia.

When the optical system and the axial length of the eye are such that light from an infinitely distant object is focused exactly on to the retina when accommodation is completely relaxed, the eye is said to be *emmetropic*, and the condition is that of emmetropia. When this is not the case the eye is said to be *ametropic*, and the three types of ametropia are *myopia, hypermetropia,* and *astigmatism.* The first two named defects are usually due to variations in the axial length of the eye-ball; and the last named due to lack of sphericity in one or more of the refracting surfaces of the eye, most frequently that of the cornea.

Figure 50 illustrates the case of emmetropia (a), myopia (b) and hypermetropia (c).

In myopia, or short sight, the refracting power of the eye or its axial length is too great and light from a very distant object is focused in front of the retina. In hypermetropia, or long sight, the refracting power or the axial length is too small and incident parallel light is focused behind the retina. In the case of astigmatism, the refracted beam from a point object will be imaged in two focal lines which may occupy any positions with respect to the retina, but in no case will the object be seen distinctly.

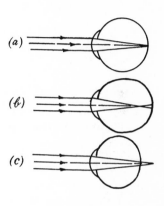

FIG. 50.

Near and Far Points.

The object point conjugate to the retina, when accommodation is completely relaxed, is known as the *far point.* This will be (a) at infinity in the case of an emmetropic eye, (b) a real object in myopia, and (c) a virtual object point behind the eye in hypermetropia.

The conjugate point to the retina when accommodation is exerted to its fullest extent, is termed the *near point;* and is the nearest position at which an object can be distinctly seen.

The Correction of Ametropia.

Myopia, or hypermetropia may be corrected by placing in front of the eye a lens that will give the light from an infinitely distant object the necessary vergence for it to be focused on the retina. As will be seen from Fig. 51 (a) the necessary condition for the correction of myopia is to place a diverging lens in front of the eye of such a power, that the light is now brought to a focus on the retina instead of in front of it; whereas in the case of hypermetropia, a converging lens of suitable power will be required (see Fig. 51 (b)).

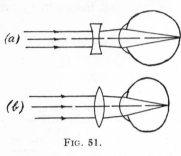

FIG. 51.

Correction of Myopia and Hypermetropia.

If astigmatism is to be corrected, it is necessary to position in front of the eye a cylindrical lens opposite in power to that existent on the refraction surfaces of the eye (e.g. on the cornea) but with its axis parallel to the cylinder on the latter.

(N.B.—The usual distance of the correcting spectacle lens from the cornea is about 20 mm.)

Working Model of the Human Eye.

The preceding remarks concerning emmetropia and ametropia can be conveniently illustrated in practical form by setting up a working model of the human eye on the optical bench.

Utilizing the metre optical bench and fittings of page 21, we may set up at one end a $+10D$ spectacle lens from the trial case and a ground glass screen 10 cm. away (see Fig. 52) to represent the eye.

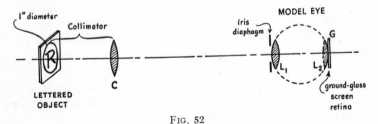

FIG. 52

Working model of Eye.

At the other end of the bench a collimator is arranged, in order to produce a very distant object for the model eye to "look at." The collimator, which may consist of some bold letter on a piece of clear glass as an object and a lens of about 10 cm. focal length, is focused for infinity as mentioned in chapter II. If the object is now illuminated with a diffuse source of light, an image of the letter should be seen sharply in focus on the ground glass screen (representing the retina). This illustrates the case of the emmetropic eye, with accommodation relaxed, looking at an infinitely distant object (i.e. the far point at infinity).

Another lens L_2 (in this case of 20 cm focus) is placed on the optical bench and arranged to slide between L_1 and the ground glass screen. By alteration of the distance between L_1 and L_2 the power of the lens system is changed, and this produces in effect the "accommodating power" for the model eye which in reality is carried out by the automatic change in curvature of the surfaces of the crystalline lens in the human eye. If, therefore, we bring the lens L_2 up in contact with L_1, this would represent the condition of maximum accommodation; and if the collimator lens C is then removed, the letter object may be brought towards L_1 until a sharp image of the letter is again seen in focus on the screen. This position of the object will represent the *near point* for the model eye. (Approximately 23 cm. from L_1.)

Let us now make the model eye myopic by increasing the distance between L_1 and G to say 12 cm. If the collimator is again put in position at the other end of the bench, it will be noticed that the letter object is no longer seen sharply defined on the ground glass screen, thus illustrating that in the case of myopia it is not possible to see very distant objects clearly.

By removing the collimator lens and bringing the object to a position where its image is seen in focus on the screen G, this will be the position of the far point (approximately 65 cm. from L_1) for the myopic eye in model form. And by placing the lens L_2 in contact with L_1 (i.e. with full accommodation exerted) the object can be brought still nearer to L_1 until its image is again seen on the screen G. The near point thus determined will be found to be 16 cm. from L_1.

We may now attempt to correct this myopic eye and restore it to the condition for normal vision. It was shown earlier that this can be done by the use of a suitable diverging (concave) spectacle lens placed in front of the eye. So that, taking the optical bench model (as we last left it) namely with the myopic eye viewing its "near point"; we can insert a number of diverging lenses (from a trial case) in turn in front of the eye until one is found which will restore the "near point position" to that already determined for the emmetropic

eye in the first experiment.   (A $-1.5D$ lens will be found suitable.)
The lens L_2 should then be removed and the collimator re-inserted,
when it will be found that the thus corrected myopic eye can now focus
very distant objects on its retina.

A similar experiment to the foregoing one may be carried out for
the illustration of hypermetropia.

In this case the length L_1G of the model eye-ball may be decreased
to (say) 8 cm. If the collimator is again set up, the image of the
letter object will fall *outside* the retina screen G and it will be necessary
to insert the correct converging lens (a $+3D$ lens) in front of the eye
in order to focus the letter sharply on the screen G. Thus the hyper-
metropic eye model will have its "far point" restored to the normal
infinite distance, whereas when L_2 is now placed in contact with L_1 (to
give the effect of full accommodation) the normal distance (23 cm.)
for the "near point" will again be found. The collimator lens is
removed of course and the object brought towards the eye as before
to obtain this reading.

To illustrate the effect of astigmatism, the lens L_1 and the screen G
should first be re-set to their positions for the model of the emmetropic
eye as in experiment No. 1. The lens L_2 should then be placed in
contact with L_1 and the object brought up to the position of the near
point. The letter object, however, should now be changed for one
consisting of radial lines (see Fig. 53). The model eye may now be

made purposely astigmatic by introducing a weak
cylindrical lens, (such as a $-0.5D$) immediately in
front of lens L_1; and on viewing the ground glass
screen G (i.e. the retina) it will be noticed that
instead of all the radial lines now being in focus,
only one or two will appear so.

Fig. 53.

The correction of this defective eye can then be
carried out by making use of the spectacle trial case,
choosing a suitable correcting cylindrical lens (namely a $+0.5D$ cyl.)
and whilst placing it in front of the eye, it must be rotated in its own
plane until *all* the radial lines are again seen in focus on the retinal
screen G. When this has been done, it will be noted that the correcting
cylinder is one which is opposite in power to that present in the
defective eye but with its axis *parallel* to the axis of the cylinder
contained in the eye.

Resolving Power.

One of the more interesting points connected with vision is the resolving power of the eye or its limit in ability to see fine detail of the object being observed; sometimes this is called the *Visual Acuity* of the eye.

Hooke, during the latter end of the seventeenth century, pointed out (from his astronomical observations) that the limit in the visual acuity angle was of the order of one minute of arc. Since that time Helmholtz* and many other workers have substantiated this statement by various subjective measurements. Although this limit may be considered by some to be rather low, it does nevertheless serve as a useful standard. This visual acuity limit of one minute of arc corresponds to an object interval of one and a half feet being just resolved by the eye at a distance of one mile, or 0·075 mm. (say one tenth of a mm.) at the nominal near point distance of 10 inches. Various subjective tests may be made to determine the visual acuity of the emmetropic eye, such as the familiar sight-testing charts (used by ophthalmic opticians) which are so arranged that the complete block letter subtends five minutes of arc at the eye for a stated distance, whilst the arm width of the letter subtends an angle of one minute. (See Fig. 54). For tests at the near point, a number of screens consisting of alternate opaque and transparent lines illuminated from behind may be employed. A range of such screens having from 50 lines per inch up to 300 lines per inch increasing in steps of say 50, will cater for the testing of a visual acuity angle of from 4 to 1 minute of arc.

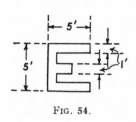

FIG. 54.

This experimental determination of the resolving power of the human eye may be well supported and indeed verified by a theory based on the diameter of the foveal cones in relation to the diameter of the Airy diffraction disc given by the eye as a lens system.

By measurement of photomicrographs taken by E. F. Fincham of the foveal region of the retina (see Fig. 55) it may be shown that each cone has a diameter of 0·0025 mm. or 2.5 microns. Now the

* Helmholtz, *Physiological Optics* (English translation), Vol. 1, p. 176.

diameter of the Airy diffraction disc of a lens system may be taken as

$$\frac{1 \cdot 22\lambda}{N' \cdot \sin U'_M}$$

and in the case of the eye the refractive index N' of the medium in which the image is formed can be assumed as $1 \cdot 34$, whilst U'_M can be deduced from the average semi-diameter y of the pupil divided by the focal length f of the eye (see Fig. 49), namely

$$\frac{y}{f} = \frac{2}{20} = 0 \cdot 10.$$

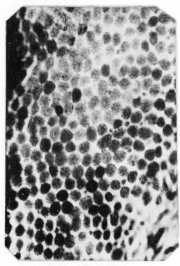

The wavelength $(\lambda) = 0 \cdot 00055$ mm.

FIG. 55.

Transverse section of Cones in the Foveal Region of the Human Retina —Photomicrograph by E. F. Finsham. Mag. × 1600.

Thus, the diameter of the Airy diffraction disc on the retina of the human eye

$$= \frac{1 \cdot 22 \times 0 \cdot 00055}{1 \cdot 34 \times 0 \cdot 10} = 0 \cdot 0050 \text{ mm.}$$

The theory put forward by Hering* was based on the assumption that if two diffraction discs (corresponding to two very close object points) were formed on the foveal region of the retina, it would be necessary to have at least one foveal cone between the centres of the diffraction discs in order to carry a stimulus to the brain which would enable the discs to be seen separately; or in other words that the two object points might be resolved.

This very natural assumption is illustrated in a diagrammatic drawing in Fig. 56 in which two diffraction discs are shown superimposed on the foveal cone mosaic and separated by a distance equal to twice the diameter of a foveal cone; that is, with one cone separating the centres of the discs. The distance between the centres of the diffraction discs would therefore be 5 microns or 0·005 mm.

The angle which this distance subtends at the optical centre or nodal point of the eye is equal to 0·005 mm. divided by the length

---

* Hering. Leipzig Berichte, 1900, pp. 16-24.

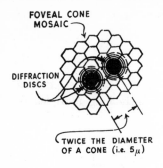

FOVEAL CONE
MOSAIC

DIFFRACTION
DISCS

TWICE THE DIAMETER
OF A CONE (i.e. 5μ)

FIG. 56.

NF' (see Fig. 49) or $\dfrac{0 \cdot 005}{15} = 0 \cdot 00033$ radian. This corresponds very closely indeed to an angle of one minute of arc, which is also the visual acuity limit determined by subjective measurement.

Thus it would appear that the foregoing is likely to be a satisfactory theoretical explanation of the resolving power of the human eye. There are, however, other modifications of this theory based on more recent researches, and the reader will do well to consult a number of references given in W. D. Wright's *Perception of Light* (published by Messrs. Blackie and Son Ltd.).

CHAPTER IV

THE TELESCOPE

The telescope, in its various forms, is of such general use that its principle should be thoroughly understood. This is best done by making up working models of the varying types of telescopes by means of the optical bench and spectacle lenses from a trial case already described, for in this way one can have access to the various optical components and vary the distances of the latter and so illustrate the effects clearly. The external tube or mount of the complete telescope frequently hides the internal lenses and only mystifies the student; so that whilst it is, of course, advisable to take measurements on and to dissemble the complete instruments at a later period, it is more helpful in the earlier stages to make the necessary diagrammatic sketches and calculations and to make up the models according to the specifications thus arrived at. The following experiments are arranged with this in view.

Model Telescopes.

The experiment consists in setting up a simple astronomical or inverting telescope and taking measurements in connection with the instrument and then repeating the measurements for a Galilean telescope.

Astronomical Telescope.

Use a metre optical bench for the experiment. At the left hand end, place a lens (from the trial case) of fairly long focal length,

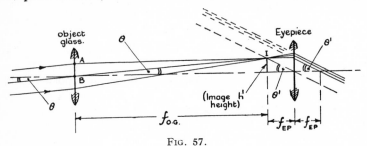

FIG. 57.

Path of Rays in Astronomical Telescope (Diagrammatic).

e.g., a + 2D, in one of the lens holders. Receive an image of some distant object produced by the lens on the ground glass screen. Place in a second holder and on the other side of the ground glass screen a short focal length lens, such as a + 12D. Turn the optical bench completely round and again focus the distant object on to the ground glass screen by adjusting the position of this lens holder. Then remove the ground glass screen from out of its mount, and insert in its place a metal diaphragm having a hole in it of about five-eighths of an inch in diameter. Now look at the distant object through the system of the two lenses. This is a simple form of inverting or astronomical telescope; the + 2 D. lens would be known as the object-glass, while the + 12 D. is the eyepiece. (See Fig. 57.) Some form of cover placed over the optical bench between the lenses will help in removing stray light and thus improve the contrast of the image.

Observe that:—

(i) The image is larger than the object as seen directly, i.e., it subtends a greater angle at the eye.

(ii) The image is inverted and reversed.

Measure the distances, off the optical bench, from the object-glass to the image, and from the eye-lens to the image, and compare these values with the nominal focal-lengths of the two lenses as given by the focal power engraved on the lens ring.

Focal length (in cm.) = 100/power (in dioptres).

Observe that the distance apart of the lenses when the telescope is focused for parallel light is equal to the sum of the focal-lengths. In this condition the telescope is said to be in " normal " or " afocal " adjustment.

Find the position with a ground-glass screen of the image of the O.G. aperture projected by the eye-lens. This image is variously known as the Ramsden circle, the eye-ring, or the exit-pupil. Note that for comfortable vision this image must fall on the pupil of the eye of the observer.

Magnifying Power.

This may be defined as the ratio:—

$$\frac{\text{angle under which the image is seen through the instrument}}{\text{angle under which the object is seen by the unaided eye.}}$$

In order to understand clearly the way in which the magnified image is produced by means of the telescope, the student should make a diagram for himself on the lines shown in Fig. 57. Parallel rays from the distant object are drawn meeting the object glass under an angle θ. The ray BI passes through the optical centre of the O.G. and is therefore undeviated; the ray AI is parallel to the axis. Where these two rays intersect, the image I (of the distant object) will be formed. This image is at the focus of the eyepiece and therefore the ray AI, if continued on parallel to the axis, will, after passing through the eyepiece lens, intersect the axis at the other focal point of the latter, and all other rays passing through I will emerge parallel to this direction. The virtual magnified image seen through the telescope will be seen under the angle θ', which may be expressed as h'/f_{EP} where h' is the height of the image at I.

The angle under which the object is seen directly by the eye alone is (neglecting the length of the telescope) h'/f_{OG}.

Hence, the magnifying power $= \dfrac{h'/f_{\text{EP}}}{h'/f_{\text{OG}}} = \dfrac{f_{\text{OG}}}{f_{\text{EP}}}$

Magnification—Direct Determination.

Use the telescope as already set up, observe through it with one eye a distant vertical scale (see Fig. 64) whilst with the other eye view the scale directly. Note how many divisions of the scale, seen by the unaided eye, are covered by a single division as seen through the telescope. The number of divisions thus seen in the space of

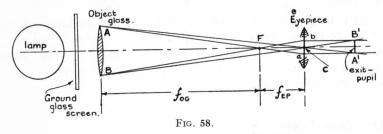

FIG. 58.

Ray Path for Formation of Exit-Pupil.

one magnified division is equal to the magnifying power of the telescope. Compare this result with the calculated value of the magnifying power obtained by dividing the focal length of the O.G. by that of the eyepiece lens.

Determination of the Magnifying Power from the Diameters of the Entrance- and Exit-pupils.

Illuminate the O.G. with diffused light, by placing a frosted lamp close to it. Place a ground-glass screen in one of the optical bench fittings, and receive an image of the O.G. aperture projected by the eye-lens, on to it. Measure the size of this image with a milli-metre scale, using a hand magnifier to help in observations. Also measure the diameter of the O.G. (with a pair of dividers). Then,

$$\text{the magnifying power} = \frac{\text{diameter of entrance-pupil}}{\text{diameter of exit-pupil}}.$$

The reason for this will be clear by referring to the diagram in Fig. 58. The exit-pupil A'B' (being an image of the object-glass AB formed by the eyepiece) will be found by drawing rays from A and B passing through the optical centre C of the eyepiece lens; these rays will pass on undeviated. And by drawing rays from A and B passing through the focus F; these will emerge parallel to the axis.

Their intersection at A′ and B′ will give the position and size of the exit-pupil, and from similar triangles
$AB/ab = f_{OG}/f_{EP}$ (and $A'B' = ab$).

From previous experiment $f_{OG}/f_{EP} = $ magnifying power.

Therefore $AB/A'B' = $ Magnifying Power $= \dfrac{\text{Diameter of entrance-pupil}}{\text{Diameter of exit-pupil.}}$

Measurement of Field of View.

Direct the telescope towards some distant wall (not less than 50 yards away) and observe what positions on the latter just appear on the extreme edges of the field when viewing through the eyepiece. An assistant can mark these positions with chalk. By measuring the distance L apart of the chalk lines and the distance D of the wall from the O.G. of the telescope, the value $L/2D$ will give the tangent of the semi-angular field of view.

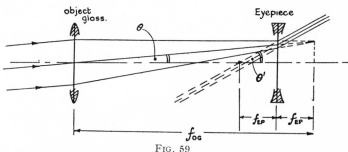

FIG. 59

Path of Rays in Galilean Type Telescope (Diagrammatic).

By determining the diameter of the diaphragm placed in the focal plane of the eyepiece and dividing this by the focal length of the object glass, this will also give the angular field, and may be used as a check on the previous determination.

Galilean Telescope.

Set up on the metre optical bench, a + 4D. lens in a holder at about the middle of the bench. Receive an image of a distant object, produced by this lens on a ground glass screen. Put a − 10 D. lens in a holder and place it on the bench *between* the O.G. and the ground glass screen, at a distance equal to the focal length of the negative lens (namely, 10 cm.) from the latter. Observe the distant object through the telescope and adjust the position of the eye lens until the object is sharply in focus. Place a cover over the space between the lenses. This is now a simple form of Galilean telescope. (See Fig. 59.)

Observe that:—

(i) The image is larger than the object as seen directly, i.e., it subtends a greater angle at the eye.

(ii) The image is erect and not reversed as in the case of the simple astronomical telescope.

(iii) The eye must be kept close up to the negative lens, and that by moving the eye from side to side an extended field may be obtained, although its angular value remains constant.

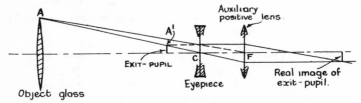

FIG. 60.
Measurement of Exit-Pupil for Galilean Telescope.

Repeat the same measurements with the Galilean telescope as mentioned before with the astronomical telescope, and tabulate the results.

A diagram illustrating the manner in which the magnified image is formed in a Galilean telescope is given in Fig. 59. Magnification =

$$\frac{\text{Angle under which image is seen through telescope}}{\text{Angle under which object is seen by unaided eye}} = \frac{\theta'}{\theta} = \frac{h'/f_{EP}}{h'/f_{OG}} = \frac{f_{OG}}{f_{EP}}$$

The measurement of the exit-pupil, in the case of the Galilean telescope, has to be carried out in another way to that employed for the astronomical type, for the exit-pupil is virtual and lies on the object glass side of the negative lens and not outside the telescope proper. Fig. 60 illustrates the ray diagram for finding the position of the exit-pupil, in which one ray is drawn from A passing through the optical centre C of the negative lens, and a second ray from A passing through the focus F. This latter ray will emerge parallel to the axis and if projected back will intersect the former ray at A'. To measure its size place a positive lens at F equal in focal length to CF, and arrange a ground glass screen to receive a real image of the exit-pupil.   This image will not necessarily be of the same size as the exit-pupil, but the diameter should be noted; and having determined afterwards the magnification given by the auxiliary positive lens with the ground glass screen at the same distance as used in the experiment, the true size of the exit-pupil may be obtained.

Huygenian Eyepiece.

This form of eyepiece is employed in many sighting instruments which are used for observational work, chiefly on account of the absence of colour fringes to the image in the outer parts of the field.   In other words this eyepiece suffers less from chromatic difference of magnification than other forms.   The eyepiece consists of two

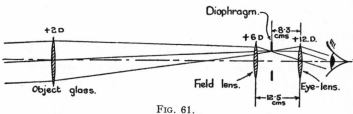

FIG. 61.
Huygenian Eyepiece Model.

plano-convex lenses, the field-lens having approximately twice the focal length of the eye-lens, with a separation equal to one-and-a-half times the focus of the latter.

A model of this can be made up by employing two spectacle lenses of +6D. and +12D. arranged in holders on the optical bench and separated in distance by 12·5 cm.   (See Fig. 61.)   At the focus of the +12D. (namely, 8·3 cm. from it) place the diaphragm of five-eighths inch diameter aperture.   The telescope objective (i.e., the +2D. lens previously used) should then be placed on the optical bench and adjusted so that its focal plane lies in the plane of the diaphragm.   In this way one can observe the appearance of some distant test-object and compare the results given by this telescope with those given by the telescope with one eye-lens only.   The effect of the field lens (the +6D. lens) may be clearly seen and it will be noted that the exit-pupil moves up much closer to the eye-lens and thus facilitates the location of the eye, whilst at the same time its size has been changed.

Ramsden Eyepiece.

In this type of eyepiece, field-lens and eye-lens have similar focal lengths, but are separated by a distance equal to seven-tenths of the focal length of either lens. Set up two +7 D. lenses and space

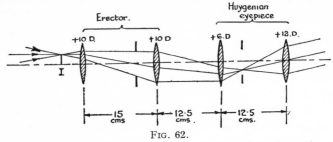

FIG. 62.

Model of Four Lens Terrestrial Eyepiece (Ray Diagram).

them by a distance = 7/10 × (14·3 cm.) = 10 cm. (This will give the same power of eyepiece as the Huygenian.) Place the diaphragm on the bench and adjust it so that it appears sharply in focus when looking through the eyepiece system. Again put the +2 D. object-glass at the other end of the optical bench and focus a distant object on to the diaphragm. Note the position of the exit-pupil in relation to the eye-lens, also its size and observe that the focal plane of the complete eyepiece is *outside* the lens system, whereas with the Huygenian type it is between the lenses.

Four-Lens Terrestrial Eyepiece.

The introduction of a two-lens erector placed between the object-glass and eyepiece of a telescope is one way of converting the astronomical form into the terrestrial type of instrument. The principle of this so-called four lens eyepiece can be conveniently illustrated on the optical bench and the arrangement of the lenses will be seen from Fig. 62. The inverted image of some distant object is first formed on the ground glass screen at I by the +2D. object-glass. The erector in most cases consists of two lenses of similar focal length and separated by a distance equal to one-and-a-half times the focal length of either; whilst the image I is situated at a distance of one-half the focal length of either lens of the erector in front of the first lens; so that we may make up a working model by placing two +10 D. lenses in their holders on the optical bench, separating them by 15 cm.

and arranging the front lens of the erector to be 5 cm. from the image plane I. Then in two more holders set up the Huygenian eyepiece (already described), with its field-lens 12·5 cm. from the rear lens of the erector. Now return to the erector system and proceed to insert between the lenses a diaphragm, the position and size of which is important; to determine this, illuminate the whole area of the object glass by means of a diffuse source of light and find the position of a ground glass screen placed between the erector lenses so that a sharp image of the O.G. is formed on the latter. Record the position on the bench and measure the diameter of the image, which will be found to be about 7 mm. Remove the ground-glass screen and replace it by a diaphragm with the above diameter hole in it. The terrestrial telescope is now complete and by viewing through the instrument, the image of distant objects will be seen to be correctly erected and reversed.

Reflecting Telescope.

In order to illustrate in practice the principle of the reflecting telescope, the Newtonian form of this instrument may be set up with

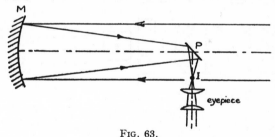

FIG. 63.
Reflecting Telescope.

the aid of the optical bench, as this is easier to demonstrate than the Gregorian or Cassegrain types, which require an opening through the main mirror.

Fig. 63 shows the arrangement of the optical parts: M is a surface-silvered mirror of about 40 cm. radius. Strictly this should be of parabolic form, but for small apertures a spherical mirror will be found quite satisfactory; and, indeed, a silvered concave spectacle lens mounted in one of the fittings may be utilized for this purpose. At about 17 cm. from the mirror is mounted a small diagonal plate P (surface-silvered) to reflect the convergent beam out at right angles to the eyepiece which observes the image at I. The whole may then be directed towards a distant object and used as a complete telescope. The improvement in the chromatic aberration will be noted when compared with the model telescopes made up with a single lens utilized as the object glass.

Measurements on Manufactured Telescopes.

Whilst the foregoing experiments in this chapter are intended to illustrate the broad principles of the telescope, the measurements and tests on the commercially manufactured instrument may need slight modification from those already described.

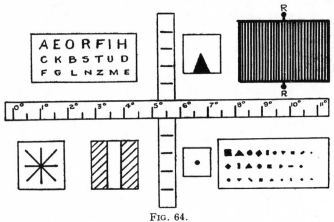

FIG. 64.

Open Field Objects for Telescope Testing.

To this end, therefore, it is desirable in the first place to have suitable test-objects set up at a convenient distance (e.g., about 100 yards) from an open window at which the observations are made. Fig. 64 shows a suggested form of such test objects which have proved satisfactory in practice. A horizontal white board with black lines at intervals corresponding to degrees of angular subtense, will be useful for the determination of the angular field of view of telescopes; whilst an arbitrary *vertical* scale will be found best for the estimation of magnification. Black letters on a white ground, radial lines, and a broad white band on a dark background (all illuminated by daylight from mirrors at the back) serve as definition tests relating to spherical aberration, astigmatism and chromatic aberration respectively. Resolving power tests may be carried out qualitatively by means of the squares, triangles and circular holes of decreasing sizes, and quantitatively by a glass plate (having alternate light and dark stripes) which can be rotated about its mid-point R. A black pointer

FIG. 65.
Altazimuth Mount for Telescope Testing.

on a white ground is suitable for tests on the so-called collimation of telescopic sights, and a mercury bulb reflecting the sun's image serves well as an artificial star for testing the aberrations of the lenses.

It is advisable to have a rigid form of support for holding the telescope to be tested; this may consist of two V brackets attached to a suitable altazimuth mounting illustrated in Fig. 65.

Magnification—Direct Observation.

Having directed the telescope towards the vertical scale of the open-field test objects (Fig. 64), the image seen through the instrument is arranged to be superimposed on the scale divisions seen directly with the other eye. By counting the number of the latter covered by (say) one division of the magnified image of the scale, will give the magnifying power of the telescope.

This simple method sometimes presents difficulty to the observer due to inability of superimposing the two images, although this is generally possible after a little practice. How-ever, an alternative method is to use a device shown in Fig. 66, which consists of a plane glass reflector R_1, and a silvered reflector R_2, arranged to be fitted over the end of the telescope eyepiece. By this means one eye alone can see the image of the scale through the telescope and simultaneously the unmagnified image; by a slight rotation of R_2 coincidence of any two lines may be made and the magnification read off.

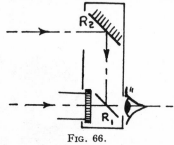

FIG. 66.

Magnification—Entrance- and Exit-Pupil Method.

The telescope may be supported in a vertical position over an illuminated white surface, and the exit-pupil observed with an eye-piece in the focal plane of which is mounted a scale divided in tenths of a millimetre. The diameter of the exit-pupil can thus be measured and this value divided into the measured diameter of the object-glass will give the magnification of the telescope, provided the whole diameter of the O.G. is being utilized. In order to check this latter point, a millimetre scale on glass may be held in contact with the front of the object glass and the exit-pupil observed where an image of this scale will be seen; the effective diameter of the O.G. can thus be measured.

In place of the scaled eyepiece a travelling microscope may be employed, and indeed this is advisable if attempting to measure the diameter of the exit-pupil of a telescope fitted with a concave eye-piece (e.g., a Galilean binocular) for the exit-pupil can only be focused by using a fairly low-power objective in the microscope as it lies on the internal side of the eyepiece.

Exit-pupil.

The diameter of the exit-pupil given by the instrument is of importance; for the brightness of the image with respect to that of the object is dependent on the area of the exit-pupil and the area of the eye-pupil. The iris diaphragm of the human eye varies in diameter according to the external illumination; for example, in bright sunlight it may be as small as two millimetres and in dull weather approximately four millimetres; whereas at night it may be as large as eight millimetres in diameter. As the area of a circle $= \pi r^2$, it will be seen that the light-gathering power of the eye is sixteen times greater for night-vision than for day-vision. Consequently, a telescope intended for night use should have an exit-pupil of at least 8 mm. in diameter, whilst for average day use 3 to 4 mm. is advisable. If the exit-pupil is smaller than the eye-pupil opening for any given conditions of illumination, the object would not appear as bright as the object seen directly by the unaided eye (neglecting losses due to absorption and reflection by the optical parts of the instrument). Thus, the ratio of brightness of the image to that of the object $= \dfrac{\text{area of exit-pupil.}}{\text{area of eye-pupil}}$

Angular Field of View.

If the telescope is set up on the altazimuth mounting and directed towards the field-object horizontal scale already calibrated in angular divisions, the field of view (real) may be read off by observing the positions at which the diaphragm of the eyepiece appear to cut the scale. (For a magnification of times 5, the field is generally of the order of five degrees, whereas for times 25, the field may be reduced to about one degree).

The apparent field of view is obtained by observing where the virtual image of the eyepiece diaphragm appears to cut the open field as seen with the other eye open. Having noted the two positions where this occurs, the angular separation of the latter is measured either by a direct reading off the scale or by setting the cross-line of the telescope in turn on these two points and reading the angular amount off the azimuth scale. The apparent field should be equal to the real field multiplied by the magnifying power of the instrument.

Types of Telescope Objectives and Eyepieces.

The chief forms of telescope objectives likely to be met with in practice are depicted diagrammatically in Fig. 67. The most usual form still encountered (originally designed by Fraunhofer) consists of a double-convex crown lens and a concave flint lens with nearly plane last surface. In this objective the primary chromatic aberration and spherical aberration is corrected and the lens is practically free from coma.

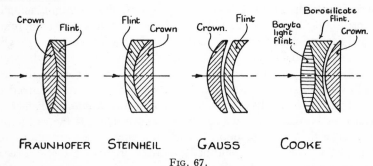

FIG. 67.

Types of Telescope Objectives.

The type in which the flint lens is situated in front is due to Steinheil. Slightly steeper curves are required for the surfaces, but the removal of the aberrations can be carried out to much the same degree as in the Fraunhofer type.

In the Gauss form, the crown lens is in front, but the contact surfaces do not have similar radii. This permits of a greater degree of freedom in the removal of the aberrations, for example, such a lens can be corrected for spherical aberration for two wavelengths.

With the three lenses of different glasses utilized in the Cooke type of objective the chromatic aberration may be corrected for three wavelengths with a consequent reduction in the secondary spectrum.

For a fuller appreciation of the methods of designing such lenses, a closer study of the detail of such processes must be made. As an aid to this A. E. Conrady's book on *Optical Design* will be found useful, but a more complete knowledge can only be attained by experience of the actual computing work involved.

In connection with eyepieces which are most commonly found in commercially-made telescopes, the well-known Huygenian and

Ramsden types (already described) still hold their place, although the former is more generally employed on account of the small chromatic difference of magnification inherent in this type. For higher-power eyepieces and when wider fields of view are required it is necessary to employ rather more complicated systems, such as

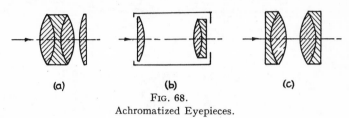

(a)   (b)   (c)

FIG. 68.

Achromatized Eyepieces.

those indicated in Fig. 68. Type (a) is the Abbe orthoscopic eye-piece, whilst (b) and (c) are two forms of the achromatized Ramsden eyepiece. The previous remarks relating to the design of the object-glasses also apply to these lens systems.

Definition Tests.

The optical performance of a telescope is necessarily of primary importance, but the judging of the quality of definition given by the instrument is not always an easy operation and depends largely on the experience of the observer. For example, highly trained men can tell (by directing a telescope towards a set of objects similar to those shown in Fig. 64) whether the instrument is giving "first quality" definition or not and also in many cases they can tell what is the cause of inferior definition should this be manifest; this judge-ment may be facilitated if an auxiliary telescope (giving an excellent performance) is kept as a standard of reference and mounted along-side the instrument under test so that alternate observation can be made and the results compared.

For less-trained observers, however, the star-test will afford an easier means of both testing the optical performance and determining the nature of the aberration if the instrument is defective.

This test consists in directing the telescope towards an artificial star and in examining the expanded out-of-focus image on both sides of the best focus. The artificial star may consist either of a steel ball reflecting an image of the sun or of a minute hole suitably illuminated

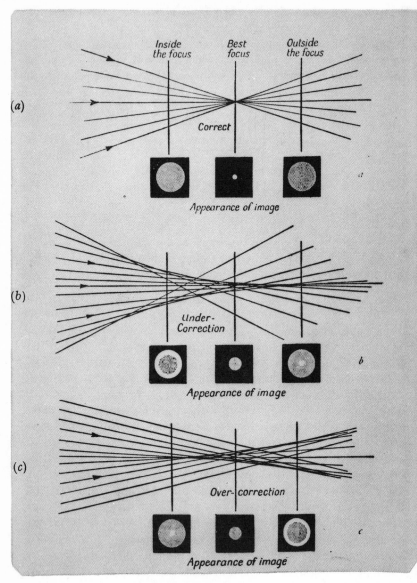

FIG. 69.
Star Test Illustrating Spherical Aberration.

in a dark corridor. (Methods for producing various forms of artificial star have been described by the author in the *Optician*, February, 1925, Vol. 69, No. 1769, pages 5-7).

The defects which may be present in a telescope objective are
(i) chromatic aberration
(ii) spherical aberration
(iii) coma
and (iv) astigmatism.

A two-lens achromatic objective (intended for visual work) is generally designed so that the red (C line) and blue (F line) are brought to a common focus, whilst the focus for green light is found nearer to the lens; consequently the expanded images of a white star would show (within the focus) a purple outer ring with a green centre and a green outer ring and purple centre outside the focus. An apochromatic objective—in which red, green and blue are brought to one focus—would show a white circular patch on each side of the focus.

For the examination of the lens for the presence of spherical aberration a monochromatic star may be used (preferably green). By referring to Fig. 69a (which is a grossly exaggerated diagrammatic illustration of the union of the rays in the image formed by the objective) it will be seen that if the rays from all parts of the objective coincided in one point (*i.e.*, freedom from spherical aberration), the appearance of the circular patch of light on each side of the best focus position would be similar.

If, on the other hand, appearances are seen resembling those in Fig. 69 (b) and (c) "under-corrected" or "over-corrected" spherical aberration would be indicated respectively.

The defect, known as coma, is caused by oblique rays through the lens not intersecting on the oblique axis pr (see Fig. 70). This produces a flared tail to an otherwise circular image of the star and gives a distinctly unpleasant appearance to images seen at the edge of the field. Should this aberration be present in the centre of the field it is more serious and should not be tolerated; it may be caused by a tilting or an error of centering of one or both the components of the objective.

Astigmatism is also an aberration due to oblique rays and may be caused by such rays in meridians at right angles to one another coming to a focus at different distances along the oblique axis. For instance, in Fig. 71 the rays in a vertical plane may come to a focus at a point A, whilst those in a horizontal plane at a point B. This would result in focal lines being formed at these positions and a circular disc of least confusion at C. The expanded images would show elliptical patches of light and this is a characteristic indication of astigmatism.

Squaring-on Test.

The optical performance of a telescope objective may be impaired by its incorrect mounting in the telescope tube; for example, both

FIG. 70.
Illustrating Coma (Diagrammatic).

coma and astigmatism may be caused by the optical axis of the O.G. not being co-linear with the axis of the tube. A device for checking this is shown in Fig. 72 and consists of a tube T (which fits *well* in the eyepiece tube of the telescope), a polished diagonal plate P and a pinhole H. If the device is now placed in the telescope eye-

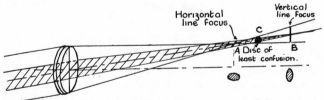

FIG. 71.
Illustrating Astigmatism (Diagrammatic).

piece tube and the diagonal plate illuminated by a diffuse source of light, virtual images of the illuminated plate (in the form of an annulus of light) will be seen reflected in the various surfaces of the objective at the other end of the tube. As the fourth radius of many objectives is usually a very long one (and sometimes flat) the reflected image from this surface appears approximately the same size as the object, and if properly squared-on would look somewhat as indicated in Fig. 73a. But if *not* squared-on the image would appear as in Fig. 73b. By tilting the lens the appearance (a) may be restored. Having secured this condition, the virtual images from

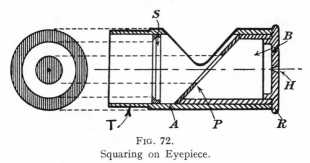

FIG. 72.
Squaring on Eyepiece.

the other lens-surfaces may be looked for; these are generally much smaller (as they are produced by reflection from relatively steeply curved convex or concave surfaces) and if the lens-components are

FIG. 73.
Appearances seen with Squaring-on Test.

properly centred, the images should all appear concentric, as shown in Fig. 73c.

Stray-Light Tests.

The presence of stray-light in optical instruments may affect their performance considerably, chiefly on account of the lack of contrast produced in the image. For example, light scattered and reflected from the walls of a telescope may not enter the eye when the instrument is used in daylight (*i.e.*, when the iris of the eye is about 3 to 4 mm. in diameter), but in fading light or in darkness when the pupil is expanded to perhaps 8 mm. diameter, such stray light will often cause troublesome effects, amounting sometimes to inability of picking up distant objects owing to lack of contrast in the field.

A convenient way of testing this defect is to direct the instrument towards an illuminated diffusing screen on which is mounted a

circular black patch of opaque material (see Fig. 74). Its diameter
and distance from the telescope object glass should be such that the
exit-pupil of the instrument is just " blacked-out " when viewed
with a hand magnifier.

Any stray-light or ghost images will be apparent by observation
of the exit-pupil in this way and may, if desired, be photographed.
Fig. 75 shows such a photograph and illustrates how serious this
defect may be in a prismatic binocular.

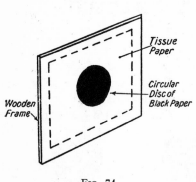

FIG. 74.

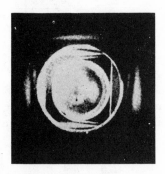

FIG. 75.
Exit-Pupil of a Prismatic Binocular
photographed and enlarged showing
Stray and Scattered Light.

The proper use of screening the prism edges and the adequate
employment of diaphragms will help in the removal of reflected light.

Test for Strain.

It is of importance that none of the optical parts of a telescope
system should show signs of being strained, for otherwise the definition of the instrument may be impaired, sometimes producing a
doubling of the image if the strain is severe. Strain can quite un-
wittingly be produced by clamping a lens too tightly in its cell, for
example, or a prism in its support. It is important, therefore, to
avoid such distortion of the glass surfaces.

Consequently, the various components (lenses or prisms) in their
mounts or the completely assembled instrument are examined in
polarised light, when strain will be revealed by the presence of light
patches or sometimes even colour in an otherwise dark field (*i.e.*,
when polariser and analyser are " crossed ").

A suitable form of polariscope may be made up by utilizing a reflecting surface (at the appropriate angle) as polariser and a Nicol prism as analyser. (See Figs. 76 a and b.)

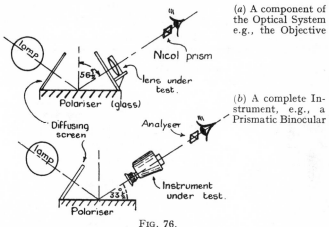

(a) A component of the Optical System e.g., the Objective

(b) A complete Instrument, e.g., a Prismatic Binocular

FIG. 76.
Examination of Optical Parts in Polarised Light.

It is of interest to examine in the polariscope a number of lenses in their mounts, especially those which may be held in their cells by spinning the metal over the glass work. Should there be the slightest trace of colour visible or even a dark cross on a light field, this should not be tolerated. Only regions of dull grey should be permitted to allow a lens through this test.

Resolving Power.

Resolving power may be defined as the ability of a lens system to reveal fine detail. It may be expressed as the angle which two just-resolved images subtend at the objective, or in terms of the minimum size of object just discerible at a given distance from the lens.

A very small distant object point viewed by a lens will give an Airy diffraction disc (see Fig. 77) at its focus. The diameter of this disc is given by $\dfrac{1.22\lambda}{N'\sin U'_{M}}$, where $\lambda =$ the wave length of the light; N' is the refractive index of the medium in the image space (usually air, and therefore N' is equal to unity) U'_{M} is the angle that the extreme marginal ray from the lens makes with the optical axis. Hence, the larger the diameter of the lens for a given focal length, the smaller will be the Airy disc. It is now a generally accepted fact that two close image points will just be seen as two separate diffraction discs when their central separation is equal to the radius of the Airy disc. Calling this value, namely, $\dfrac{0\cdot61\lambda}{N'\sin U'_{M}} = h'$ in Fig. 78, the resolving power angle θ will be h'/f' where f' is the focal length of the lens. From this it can be shown that the Resolving Power of a telescope objective is equal to $1\cdot22\lambda/A$ where A is the full aperture of the lens.

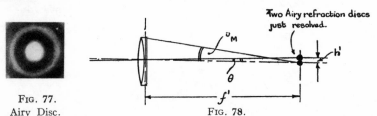

FIG. 77.
Airy Disc.

FIG. 78.

For a one inch diameter objective, this angle θ is of the order of 6 seconds of arc, whilst for a 100″ telescope the angle θ is slightly less than 0·1 second of arc. These angles correspond respectively to about one inch at a thousand yards, and 127 yards at 240,000 miles (e.g., the distance of the moon). A convenient way of obtaining a numerical value for the resolving power of a telescope is to direct the instrument towards an object consisting of alternate clear and opaque stripes (in effect a course grating) illuminated by daylight from behind (as indicated in Fig. 64) and then to rotate this grating about an axis parallel to the lines until the latter cease to be visible. Thus the object interval when resolution ceases will be the known separation of the lines multiplied by the cosine of the angle through which the grating has been moved.

The experiment may be carried out either in the form of an open-field type of object or in the laboratory, where a long corridor is available. The set-up of the apparatus can be arranged as indicated in Fig. 79, the telescope viewing the grating object via the plane mirror M. The purpose of the latter is to allow the grating to be near the observer so that he can rotate it himself whilst observing. The mirror M should have a good quality flat surface (silvered on the front), and if the distance D is 100 yards the size of the grating G would require to be approximately 3 feet by 2 feet.

Such an object area may not occupy the whole angular field of the telescope, but this is not essential as it is only in the centre of the field where such a critical test as resolving power would be made. The grating itself may be produced by painting black stripes (utilizing a stencil for doing this) on a piece of plate glass of the size already indicated, making the clear spaces equal in interval to the opaque portions.

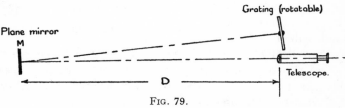

FIG. 79.
Resolving Power Test for Telescopes.

For objectives of one inch aperture and at a distance $2 \times D = 200$ yards the strips would require to be one fifth of an inch wide, whilst for a two inch diameter lens the strip width would have to be of the order of a one tenth of an inch.

As the grating is also rotatable, the apparent separation of the lines may be decreased until resolution ceases.

If the experiment is to be carried out in a corridor indoors with the object at a much closer distance (e.g., $D = 25$ yards, say) one can use a piece of Process Screen (6in. square), having 50 lines per inch on it. This mounted on a rotating table, such as a spectrometer circle, would serve the purpose well.

Such an experiment is an excellent one, more especially if an iris diaphragm is fitted over the objective of the telescope, so that the resolving power may be measured for successive apertures of the lens and these results plotted.

Necessary Power of Eyepiece.

In order to do justice to the resolving power of the telescope objective it is necessary to render visible to the eye the smallest image interval given by the O.G. This is done by using the appropriate power of eyepiece. For example, the resolving power angle θ for a one inch diameter objective would be $1 \cdot 22 \times \lambda / A = 1 \cdot 22 \times 0 \cdot 000022'' / 1''$ $= 0 \cdot 000027$ radians, and if its focal length is twelve inches, the value for the smallest image interval h' in Fig. 78 will be $12 \times 0.000027 = 0.00032$ inches.

This distance viewed by the unaided eye at its " near point " would subtend an angle of $0.00032/10$ radians, but as the limiting angle for normal Visual Acuity is one minute of arc (or 0.0003 radians), the necessary power of the eyepiece must be $0.0003/0.000032 = 10$ times (very closely).

And as the magnifying power of an eyepiece may be taken as $\dfrac{\text{Distance of distinct vision,}}{\text{Focal length of eyepiece}}$ the eyepiece focal length will be one inch. For slightly more comfortable vision it may be necessary to use a two minute Visual Acuity angle, in which case the eyepiece would have to be $\times 20$ or 0.5 inch focal length. The following table (I) may be found useful:—

TABLE I.

THEORETICAL RESOLVING POWER.			NECESSARY POWER OF EYEPIECE.	
Diameter of Object-Glass.	$\theta = 1.22/A$ Angle θ in radians.	Object interval just resolved at one mile.	(Assuming Visual Acuity of 1') for telescope working at $F/10$	$F/15$
1″	0.000027	1.70″	× 11	× 7.5
2″	0.000013	0.85″	× 22	× 15
3″	0.0000089	0.57″	× 33	× 22.5
4″	0.0000067	0.42″	× 44	× 30
6″	0.0000044	0.28″	× 66	× 45

Binocular Telescopic Instruments.

The chief advantage of the binocular telescope over the monocular type, is that both eyes can be employed for observation and the consequent stereoscopic power of the eyes maintained and in certain cases enhanced. Moreover, by the use of prisms in the two telescopes the effective length of the instrument is reduced, making it more compact; whilst at the same time providing a means for erecting the image.

The stereoscopic range for normal binocular vision of the unaided eyes varies from the Near Point (namely, ten inches from the eyes) up to approximately 350 yards. Beyond this distance, it is difficult to decide (for example) whether one object (similar in size to the other) is nearer or farther from the observer, except only by our previous experience and knowledge of the size of such objects. An interesting experiment may be carried out to determine the minimum distance δ (see Fig. 80) between two objects placed in front of one another, it is possible to detect for various distances R. Three rods, A, B, C (in Fig. 80) of the same diameter are screened so that only a

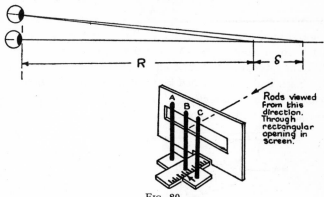

FIG. 80.
Stereoscopic Range for Binocular Vision.

limited portion of them is visible to the observer through a rectangular aperture. The centre rod B is moved either in front or behind A and C by an assistant whilst the observer at a measured distance (say 50 yards) signals when he can just detect that B is in front or behind A and C. In this way, taking a number of settings, a value for δ may be obtained for distances of R equal to (say) 10, 20, 40, 80 and 160 yards.

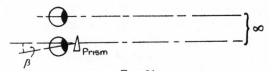

FIG. 81.
Angular Accommodation Test.

For a binocular telescope, the limit of the stereoscopic range may be taken as $R \times M \times O/E$) where
R is the limit of the stereoscopic range for the unaided eye (i.e., 350 yards),
M is the magnification of either of the telescopes,
O is the distance apart of the object-glasses
and E the distance apart of the eyepieces.

For example, if we take a prismatic binocular with O equal to 130 mm., and E equal to 65 mm., and a magnification of $\times 6$, the limit of stereoscopic range for such an instrument would be 4,200 yards; whilst the value for δ (Fig. 80) at 500, 1,000 and 2,000 yards would be 9, 35 and 140 yards respectively.

Angular Accommodation.

The use of binocular instruments requires that the two optical axes of the telescopes should be set to within certain limits, otherwise strain on the eyes will be imposed in attempting to fuse the two images. Such limits are decided by what tolerances can be permitted by a *change in axis direction* of the unaided eyes, or "angular accommodation" as it is sometimes called.

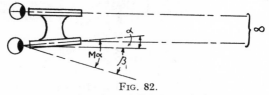

FIG. 82.
Inclination of Telescope Axis.

An experiment to illustrate and determine these tolerances can be carried out by viewing a distance object (e.g., one of those depicted in Fig. 64) with both eyes and then interposing in turn various small-angle prisms* in front of one eye. In this way the angular deviation β (Fig. 81) may be gradually increased until it is no longer possible to fuse the two images.. This should be done when the apex of the prism is pointing inwards (as in Fig. 81), giving induced convergence of the two eyes; secondly, with the apex pointing outwards, causing divergence of the axes, and thirdly when the apex is pointing upwards or downwards. The limiting value of β for the above conditions when combination of the two images becomes difficult, will vary amongst a number of observers, but the results of a large number of tests seem to indicate that for a normal person the safe limit to impose on the induced angle of accommodation is:—

Horizontal convergence $\beta = 2° 18'$ (i.e., 4 prism dioptres)
Horizontal divergence $\beta = 1° 9'$. (i.e., 2 ,,   ,,)
    and Vertical vergence $\beta = 34·5'$ (i.e., 1 prism dioptre).

* A selection of such prisms may be found in a good quality spectacle trial case varying from 1 to 10 dioptres.

The importance of the foregoing facts has a bearing on the construction and adjustment of binocular instruments; for, whilst in practice perfect parallelism of the two telescope axes may be unattainable, the eyes will be able to adjust themselves to give a single impression of the object observed, provided the error of parallelism of the axes does not exceed a certain amount. The relation between this amount and the angular accommodation limit of the unaided eyes can be deduced in the following way.

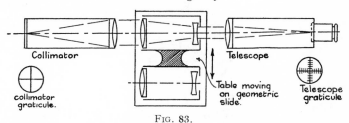

FIG. 83.

Apparatus for Testing Axis Parallelism of Binocular Instruments
(Diagrammatic).

Let the inclination of the telescope axes be α (Fig. 82) and M their magnifying power. Then the emergent beam from the eyepiece will be deviated by $M\alpha$. Therefore the deviation β from the parallel will be $\beta = M\alpha - \alpha = \alpha \ (M-1)$. Thus, if β is the maximum angle through which it is safe to induce angular accommodation; then α (the angle between the telescope axes) is

$$\alpha = \frac{\beta}{M-1}$$

The following table gives the permissible error in parallelism of the optical axes of the two telescopes for a binocular instrument, based on the values of β given on page **70**.

TABLE II.

Magnification.	Permissible error in Parallelism. (minutes of arc)		Vertical Allowance.
	Horizontal Allowance		
	Convergence.	Divergence.	
× 3	69'	34'	17'
× 6	28'	14'	7'
× 10	15'	8'	4'
× 12	13'	6'	3'

Apparatus for Adjusting Binocular Telescopes.

Various mechanical devices have been made for testing the parallelism of the telescope axes, but the main principle consists in having a collimator and telescope arranged so that they are co-axial (see Fig. 83) and adjusted so that the image of the collimator cross-line

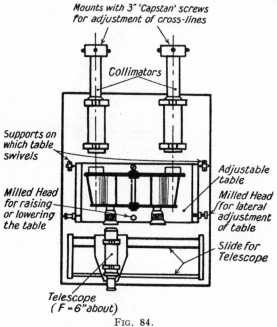

FIG. 84.

coincides with the cross-line graticule of the telescope. The instrument to be tested is clamped firmly on to a suitable table, which is mounted on an accurately made cross-slide so that each half of the binocular may be brought in turn between the telescope and collimator. If the graticule cross-line of the telescope is marked with divisions corresponding to a known angular subtense at the object-glass (e.g., 3 minutes of arc), the error in parallelism of the axes (both lateral and vertical) may be read off directly. The instrument can then be adjusted until both errors are within the permissible tolerances. An alternative device is shown in Fig. 84, in which two parallel collimators are employed and the telescope is made moveable. A form of testing-bench which is more generally practicable, however, is depicted in Fig. 85, which incorporates the advantages of both the foregoing examples; for by having both table and telescope moveable (as illustrated) a more varied type of binocular may be accommodated irrespective of the distance apart of the object-glasses or eyepieces.

Rotation of Image.

When testing prismatic binocular instruments on such a bench it

FIG. 85.
Binocular Testing Bench for Prismatic or Galilean Forms.

may be noted that the image of the collimator cross-line appears rotated with respect to the telescope cross-line. This defect (sometimes known as incorrect inversion) is caused by the two prisms of a Porro system (for example) not being at right angles to one another, as indicated in Fig. 86. The angular rotation of the image will be just double that of the prism error, so that adjustment in this respect is critical; for rotational effects cannot be tolerated.

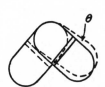

Plan view of 2 right-angled Prisms as used in a Binocular showing an error 'θ' which produces bad inversion effect.

FIG. 86.

Wide Field of View Sighting Telescopes.

Most normal telescopes, having magnifications of from about twenty times to three times, usually have fields of view extending from one and a half degrees to about nine or ten degrees. In certain cases, however, it is necessary to have a larger field, say, twenty degrees, and, moreover, in some kinds of work (e.g., in periscopes) such telescopes may be required to have long and narrow tubes into which the optical system has to be fitted. Other examples are the instruments used for examination of internal parts of the human body, such as cystoscopes, for example. Whilst one cannot give, in a book of this size, the full optical details of each of these various instruments, the general principles of their construction may be understood from the following remarks.

Referring to Fig. 87. an object-glass A (taking in the necessary angular field) forms an inverted image of the distant object in the plane of a field-lens B. The focal length of the latter is such that an image of lens A is formed on lens C, thus collecting all the light that enters the objective (e.g. if $f_B = \dfrac{f_A}{2}$ and the distance $AB = BC = 2f_B$ this would serve). Lens C is an erecting lens of (say) the same focal length of lens B and with the distance $BC = CD = 2f_C$, thus

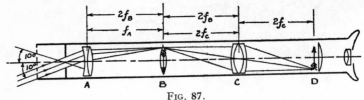

FIG. 87.
Wide Angular Field Telescope.

collecting all the light from lens B and giving an erect image of the distance object in the focal plane D of the eyepiece. If desired another lens could be placed at D and the general procedure of forming an image of the preceding lens (in this case C) on to the next lens in the optical train, may be carried out to suit any desired length of the external tube of the instrument.

It will be found helpful to illustrate this principle by making up a model on the metre steel rule optical bench and using spectacle trial case lenses. Although such lenses will not give such good definition as the properly corrected ones, the general principle and lay-out may be readily tried out. The following lenses will be found suitable: For lens A (Fig. 87) use a +5D. lens; at a distance of 20 cm. from A place a + 10D. lens in its holder and then another +10D. lens at C, 20 cm. from B. The image of a distant object will then be formed at D 20 cm. from C and may be focused on a ground glass screen. In place of the latter it is better to substitute an Huygenian eyepiece (a model of which is shown in Fig. 61) so that the image at D will now have a + 12D. lens at 8·5 cm. to the right of it and a + 6D. lens (as field lens) 4 cm. in front of it. The whole model thus set up on the optical bench may be directed towards the distant angular scale and the image observed. By placing 4 cm. in front of the lens A a diaphragm having a hole (one third of an inch in diameter) a general correction in the whole lens-system will occur, with a consequent improvement in definition. Added interest will be given to the experiment, if lenses of + 9D. and + 12D. are substituted in turn for the lens A and note taken of the increase in angular field of the instrument, but also of course the reduction in magnification.

Another way of producing a wide-angle telescope system is to employ the optical parts arranged as in Fig. 88, which shows two

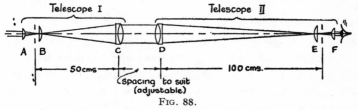

FIG. 88.
Another Form of Wide-Angle Telescope.

telescopes placed with their object-glasses facing one another. The use of a reversed telescope (Telescope I) with Huygenian eyepiece towards the object enables a fairly wide field of view to be taken in, which may be varied by substituting a different power of eyepiece. The magnification of the complete instrument will depend on the ratio of the focal lengths of objective D to objective C (providing the eyepieces are of the same power). As the light in the space between these two last named lenses will be " parallel," a suitable separation of the two telescopes may be arranged to meet the desired requirements. For example, this optical system is sometimes employed for long periscopes having adjustable lengths, the latter corresponding to a change in space-length CD; the separation of eyepiece and objective in each telescope must of course remain fixed. When used as a periscope, the optical axis would be vertical and right angled prisms are mounted either between the lenses of eyepieces or just outside.

It will be found instructive to make up a model of this instrument, and for this purpose we may use the steel optical bench as before, but one of two metres in length (as described in Chapter II). The spectacle lenses required would be two + 12D. and two + 6D. lenses to make up the Huygenian eyepieces at either end of the optical bench. Lens C and D may be + 2D. and + 1D. respectively and should be arranged so that their focal points lie in the plane of the diaphragms in the eyepieces. The complete model (with exception of prisms which are not necessary to illustrate the principle) can now be directed towards the distant angular scale when the field-of-view and magnification can be measured. One may then experiment in the possible variations of this system by altering first the focal lengths of the lens D; then by altering the separation between C and D and finally by substituting a higher or lower power eyepiece for lens combination AB.

Variable-Power Telescopes.

Under this heading is included telescopes which, as a self-contained unit, are able to vary their magnification, and not those which alter their power merely by the substitution of a different power of eyepiece.

The principle of two of the more usual types involves that of interposing a moveable erector lens system between the image formed by the object-glass and the eyepiece. In one case the erector and eyepiece move in conjunction with one another by a suitable mechanical device so that the image always remains in focus; in the other case the eyepiece is kept stationary whilst the erector (consisting of two lenses) both moves as a whole and simultaneously the separation of the lenses is altered in such a manner that again the image remains in focus.

We can make up working models of these two types by resorting to the metre steel scale optical bench and the spectacle lenses. Using a + 3D. lens as object-glass placed at one end of the bench (Fig. 89) and directing the latter towards the distant test-objects, an image of these will be formed on a ground glass screen placed at 33.3 cm. from the O.G. At the other end of the optical bench the Huygenian eyepiece already described may be set up. As an erector lens, a + 10D. can be inserted at 13 cm. from the ground glass screen, and if the latter is now removed the telescope thus produced will give a magnification which can be measured directly (as explained on page 48. This will be found to be about × 12. If the +10D. erector is then moved to a distance of 16 cm. from the position previously occupied by the ground-glass screen, the eyepiece (as a unit)

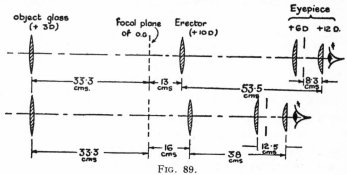

FIG. 89.
Variable-Power Telescope (Optical Bench Model).

must be brought in from the end of the bench by 15·5 cm. The distant scale is again viewed and the magnification measured, which will be found to be approximately × 6.

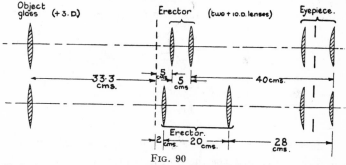

FIG. 90
Variable-Power Telescopes—Change in Separation of Erector Lenses
(Optical Bench Model).

The second type of variable-power telescope is depicted in Fig. 90. in which O.G. and eyepiece are separated by a fixed distance of 83.3 cm. on the optical bench. The erector system (in model form) is made up by using two +10D. lenses, being separated in one case by 5 cm. and in the other by 20 cm.; the distances of the front lens of the erector from the focal plane of the objective being indicated in the figure. The magnifications will be found to be × 14 and × 4 respectively.

N.B.—It may be advisable to insert a diaphragm having a hole of 0.3 in. diameter at the appropriate position between the two lenses of the erector in order to reduce the aberrations produced by the uncorrected lenses employed.

CHAPTER V

THE MICROSCOPE

The microscope is generally employed when we require to see an object or portion of an object which is too small to be seen clearly by the unaided eye. We are immediately concerned, therefore, with the way in which the size of the retinal image can be varied. The apparent size of an object is determined by the size of its image formed on the retina of the eye, and although we have no scale on the retina to measure this directly it can be determined indirectly by measuring the angle which that object subtends at the optical centre (or nodal point) of the eye. Thus, in Fig. 91 the apparent size of the object h is represented by the *visual angle* θ, which can be measured by expressing it in the term h/l (in circular measure). In

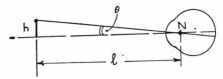

FIG. 91
Apparent Size of an Object.

order, therefore, to see an object as large as possible with the unaided eye it is necessary to place the object as near to the eye as possible compatible with distinct vision, i.e., at the " near point." This least distance of distinct vision is now conventionally taken as 10 inches or 250 millimetres for normal vision, and may be denoted as D_v, in which case the maximum apparent size of our object h will now be h/D_v (radians).

Visual Acuity.

It is interesting to attempt to measure the smallest sized object just visible to the human eye before calling in any optical aid. To do this, one can make (photographically) or obtain a number of screens consisting of alternate opaque and transparent lines varying from 100 lines per inch up to 300 lines per inch, increasing by steps of, say, 40 lines per inch. If these screens are held in turn against a fairly brightly (10 ft.-c.) illuminated matt surface at ten inches from the eye, it will be possible to decide on which screen the lines are just visible. Most observers find that they can see 260 lines per inch (or about one tenth of a millimetre) which corresponds quite closely to the accepted Visual Acuity angle of one minute of arc for the human eye. Some, however, find they can only see 140 lines per inch, which corresponds to a visual acuity of two minutes of arc.

Magnification.

Optical instruments which are used for magnifying an object, are means whereby the retinal image of the object is increased and the ratio of the size of this image to that of the object seen directly is termed the magnifying power of the instrument. This may be written:—

$$\text{Magnifying power of instrument} = \frac{\text{visual angle of image seen with instrument}}{\text{visual angle of object seen directly}}$$

Hand Magnifier or Simple Microscope.

If a small object is placed in the focal plane of a short-focus lens which is held in front of the eye, a magnified virtual image of the

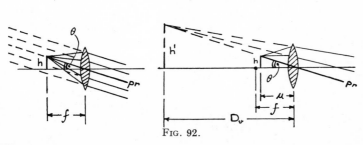

Fig. 92.

object is seen. This image is seen apparently at an infinite distance (see Fig. 92a). If the object is placed just *inside* the focus the visual image can be formed in a plane at a distance $D_v = 10''$ (see Fig. 92b). The inclination of the principal rays (pr) leaving these lenses and entering the eye, decides the angle θ under which the final image is seen and therefore θ is dependent on h/f in one case and h/u in the other.

Hence the magnification (case a) $= \dfrac{h/f}{h/D_v} = D_v/f$

and in case (b) magnification $= \dfrac{h/u}{h/D_v} = D_v/u$

(where $u = \dfrac{1}{(1/f + 0\cdot 10)}$ in inches).

But as the distances f and u do not differ widely the magnifying power of the hand lens does not change greatly, whether the virtual image is formed at infinity or at the " near point." That there is a slight difference, however, will be manifest by the following Table III, and if accurate measurements are required the magnification at

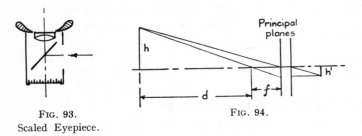

Fig. 93.
Scaled Eyepiece.

Fig. 94.

the distance D_v should be taken; for in microscope work a standard distance (at which the image is to be formed) must be fixed, and this is quite naturally taken as 10 inches from the eye on account of the fact that the object appears as large as possible at this distance before optical aid is sought.

TABLE III.

Focal Length.	Object Distance when Image is formed at D_v.	Magnifying Power.	
		Image at D_v. $M = D_v/u$.	Image at Infinity $M = D_v/f$.
2″	1·67″	× 6	× 5
1″	0·91″	× 11	× 10
0·67″	0·625″	× 16	× 15
0·5″	0·48″	× 21	× 20
0·4″	0·38″	× 26	× 25

There are many and varied types of " simple microscope " to be obtained. First, there is the ordinary hand magnifier mounted in a suitable handle and intended for general observations on almost any kind of object; many of these consist of single lenses, although most modern types are corrected for chromatic and spherical aberrations and are expected to have a flat field. The latter type are frequently mounted above a microscope stage and used for dissecting work. A further application is to mount a glass scale (usually 10 mm. divided into 100 parts) in the focal plane of the magnifier so that the scale lies in the same plane as the object, which is illuminated by a plane glass reflector (see Fig. 93).

In order to obtain the magnifying power given in the last column of Table III, a knowledge of the focal length of the lens is necessary. To determine this, an object (consisting of a piece of white card 3 feet long held against a dark background) may be set up at a distance of about 10 feet from the eyepiece. The reduced image h' (Fig. 94) of this is observed and measured by means of an auxiliary eyepiece

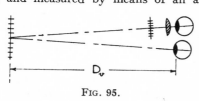

FIG. 95.

having a glass scale in its focal plane (as described above). By measuring up the distance d, the three quantities h, h' and d will be known, from which the focal length f can be found; for from the figure $f/h' = d/h$. Alternatively, the focometer (mentioned on page 35) may be employed for this measurement.

A direct method for obtaining the values in column three of Table III, is to utilize two millimetre scales on white celluloid, setting up one at 10 inches from the left eye and observing the other scale with the magnifier (see Fig. 95) and right eye. By suitable adjustment the virtual image seen by the right eye can be seen superimposed on the scale seen with the left and the magnification read off directly.

Compound Microscope.

The formation of the image seen with the compound microscope will be understood from the ray diagram (Fig. 96). The objective projects an enlarged inverted image h' of the object h, thus giving a primary (linear) magnification of

$$h'/h = g/f_0 \text{ so that } h' = h \times g/f_0. \qquad . \qquad . \qquad (1)$$

The distance g between the adjacent focal planes of the objective and eyepiece is known as the *optical tube length*. Thus the "primary magnification"

$$h'/h = \frac{\text{optical tube length}}{\text{focal length of objective}}.$$

The image h' is viewed by an eyepiece of focal length, say f_e, and the resultant virtual image is seen at an infinite distance or at any distance between infinity and the "near point" (i.e., D_v) as desired.

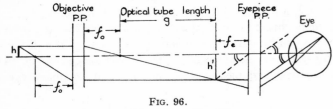

FIG. 96.

Compound Microscope—Ray Diagram.

In the former case, the angle under which the final image will be seen is h'/f_e, which from (1) gives $h \times g/(f_0 \times f_e)$. But if the object were viewed by the unaided eye at the normal distance of distinct vision D_v, it would be seen under the angle h/D_v. Hence, the magnification of the compound microscope =

$$\frac{\text{(visual angle of image seen with instrument)}}{\text{(visual angle of object seen with unaided eye)}}.$$

$$= \frac{h \times g/(f_0 \times f_e)}{(h/D_v)} \qquad = \frac{g \times D_v}{f_0 \times f_e}$$

Alternatively, the total magnifying power of the microscope may be expressed as the primary magnification multiplied by the power of the eyepiece, the latter being that given in either column three or four of Table III, depending on whether the final image is formed at D_v or at infinity respectively.

As a standard optical tube length of 160 mm. is now universally adopted, Table IV gives the nominal primary magnification for a range of objectives.

It will be understood that the values for the total magnifying power obtained from the foregoing are nominal values and will serve for most observational work. But should more accurate values be required, for example, when measuring the exact size of some object, it is necessary to measure both the primary and total magnification directly (as described later).

TABLE IV

Focal Length of Objective.	Primary Magnification.
2″ or 50 mm.	3·2
1″ or 25 mm.	6·4
$\frac{2}{3}$″ or 16 mm.	10
$\frac{1}{3}$″ or 8 mm.	20
$\frac{1}{6}$″ or 4 mm.	40
$\frac{1}{12}$″ or 2 mm.	80

Optical Bench Model of Microscope.

The principles of the microscope will be better understood by first setting up such an instrument on the steel rule optical bench and using thin spectacle lenses in place of the more complicated objectives.

Referring to Fig. 97, a millimetre scale on glass may be set up at one end of the bench and illuminated by a diffuse source of light; at 9·7 cm. from this place a +12D. lens (stopped down to a quarter-inch diameter) in a holder to serve as the microscope objective. This will form an inverted primary image of the scale 76·5 cm. away, which may be viewed by a Ramsden type eyepiece made up as on page 43, namely, utilizing two + 7D. lenses separated by 10 cm. By placing the eye behind the eyepiece the enlarged virtual image of the scale divisions will be seen; this constitutes a working model of the compound microscope.

Measurements. (Primary and Total Magnifications).

By inserting another millimetre scale on glass in the plane of the primary image, the magnification at this stage can be read off and will be found to be approximately 8 times.

If a piece of plane glass is placed at 45 degrees to the axis of the instrument so as to reflect light from the object into the eye placed as indicated in the figure, the virtual image of the scale divisions may be seen projected on to a white screen at the " near point," and a number of divisions marked out. With the eyepiece used, the

exit-pupil (i.e., the position at which the eye must be placed) is
4 cm. from the eye-lens; so that the distance of the screen from
the optical bench should be 21 cm. (see diagram), making 25 cm. or
10 in. in all $= D_v$.

By measuring up the image size on the screen of a known number
of divisions in the object, the total magnifying power may be
obtained; for the angle under which the image is seen will be h'/D_v
and the angle under which the object would be seen by the unaided
eye is h/D_v; hence $M = h'/h$. In this case the total magnification
will be found to be twenty times.

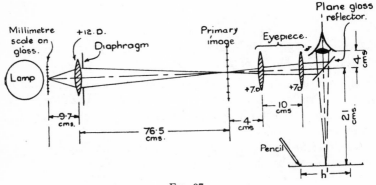

Fig. 97.
Optical Bench Model of Compound Microscope.

As the Huygenian eyepiece is more generally used in microscope
work (on account of the better state of correction for chromatic
difference of magnification) it would be well to substitute this type
(even in model form) for the Ramsden eyepiece used in the foregoing
experiment. It is interesting, however, to use the same power of
eyepiece by utilizing a $+6D$. lens placed 4 cm. in front of the
primary image plane and a $+12D$. lens 8·3 cm. behind. If the
second glass scale is again placed in a holder at the primary image
plane, it will be noted that the primary magnification has been
reduced (by the action of the field-lens) to 6·2, but when the
measurement on total magnification is repeated it will be found to
be the same as that measured when the Ramsden eyepiece was
employed.

Having carried out such measurements on the optical bench they
may be repeated with a microscope proper, using prototype objec-

tives and eyepieces. A stage micrometer and an eyepiece micro-meter would be required, and when such values have been deter-mined they may be compared with the calculated ones obtained from the nominal figures given for the focal length of the objective and the power of the eyepiece. The agreement between the latter values and the former will not necessarily be close, and for this reason (as stated earlier) it is advisable to take the direct measurement if the dimensions of an object are required with any accuracy. It will be helpful to a student for him to measure the particle size of some object (e.g., lycopodium powder) by placing it on the microscope stage after the magnification methods have been used. The average diameter of these particles will be found to be 32 microns.

Correct Setting-up of the Microscope for General Use.

The setting up of the microscope in its proper manner is a matter of importance and it is considered helpful here to enumerate the various points to be attended to. Incorrect adjustment of the instrument may lead to spurious diffraction effects in the image causing a misinterpretation of the object.

1. Arrange the microscope and source of light (an opal-bulb electric lamp in a suitable housing) in convenient positions—distance of source about 6 inches.
2. With all optical parts removed, tilt the plane mirror until the light is seen coming directly up the microscope tube.
3. Place the object on the stage, and observe same with a low-power objective (say, a two-thirds inch O.G.) and a ×15 eye-piece, setting the draw-tube to 160 mm. unless the tube-length of the O.G. is known to be otherwise.
4. Swing in the substage condenser and rack it up until the diaphragm in front of the source is seen in focus simultaneously with the object—a pencil moved about in front of the source will help this attainment.

   (*N.B.*—If an immersion objective is to be used later, it is as well to oil the slide to the condenser from the beginning—this is done by placing a small drop of immersion oil on the top lens of the condenser and then racking the latter slowly up until contact with the slide is made and the oil spreads out as a thin film.)
5. Remove the eyepiece, and close the substage iris down as small as possible. Observing the back of the objective the condenser

can now be " centred " (by means of the screw provided) until the image of the hole in the diaphragm appears concentric with the aperture of the objective.

6. With the eyepiece still removed, gradually open out the sub-stage iris until three quarters of the aperture of the objective is seen filled with light. If the object is a bold one and shows good contrast the iris should be opened until just the full aperture of the O.G. is utilized.

7. Replace the eyepiece, and observing the object, adjust the size of the diaphragm in front of the light source until all but the portion of the object immediately concerned is screened from light.

8. The instrument is now ready for critical observation of the object. A suitable light filter, complementary in colour to that of the object, may be inserted in the beam from the source.

9. The same procedure, of course, applies for the higher-power objectives, and in this case it is better to carry out the first five adjustments with a two-thirds inch objective.

(*N.B.*—When using an immersion objective a *small* drop of cedar-wood oil is placed either on the front lens of the objective or on the cover-glass, and the microscope very carefully brought down until " immersion contact " is made. Great care should be exercised in focusing or much damage can result. It is best for beginners to rack down the objective a little beyond the probable focus while watching from the side, then search for an image of the pencil point held in front of the source whilst moving the fine-adjustment in an *upwards* direction. If item No. 4 has been pro-perly carried out, the image of the object will come into focus as soon as a sharp image of the pencil point appears.)

After use the oil may be removed from the lenses with cotton-wool soaked in benzene and dried with a soft cloth (e.g., "selvyt").

Details of a suitable lamp housing, the substage unit and general items concerning illumination of the object will be found in Chapter V of *Practical Microscopy*, Martin and Johnson (Blackie and Son, Ltd.).

Focal Lengths of Microscope Objectives.

For the general construction of microscope objectives, the deter-mination of correct tube-length, the effect of change in cover-glass thickness, etc., the reader is referred to Chapter III of *Practical*

Microscopy (Martin and Johnson), but the determination of the focal-length of lens systems of such short focus is deemed advisable to be included in a book on general optics.

The method is based on the principle described on page. 31 under the heading of "magnification method," and can be carried out in practice on the microscope itself. The lens to be tested is screwed into the body tube, and an eyepiece micrometer is fitted into the draw-tube. (The latter may consist of an ordinary Huygenian eyepiece, *the field lens of which is removed*, and a one-tenth mm. glass scale placed in the focal plane of the eye-lens). A stage micrometer is then put on the instrument and focused, and the size of the image of a known interval of the object is measured up with the eye-piece—the magnification being noted down. The microscope draw-tube is then extended by, say, 30 or 40 mm. and the magnification again measured. If these two magnifications are denoted by m_1 and m_2 and the first and second positions of the draw-tube by v_1 and v_2 respectively, then the focal length f_0 will be given by

$$f_0 = (v_2 - v_1) / (m_2 - m_1).$$

Numerical Aperture.

It is now well known that the resolving power or structure-differentiating power of the microscope depends not so much upon the magnifying power as upon the "numerical aperture" of the objective.

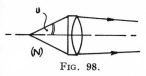

FIG. 98.

Numerical aperture (denoted N.A.) is an optical constant depending on the apical angle of the maximum cone of light which the lens can take up from a point of the object. It is defined as being equal to the product of the refractive index (N) of the medium outside the lens, and the sine of half the apical angle of the cone of light taken in by the objective, thus referring to Fig. 98.

$$\text{N.A.} = \text{N} \sin U$$

Measurement of N.A.

The determination of this value is a relatively simple procedure, especially for the so-called "dry" objectives. In this latter case the quantity N becomes unity (on account of the outside medium being air), and it only remains to measure the angle U. This may be done in several ways, but one method which can be carried out on the microscope itself is depicted in Fig. 99a. A piece of white card (with a line drawn on it) is placed on the stage and on it is rested a metal distance-piece one inch in length. With the objective to be tested screwed in the body-tube and an eyepiece in the draw-tube, the top surface of the metal gauge is focused. The gauge and eyepiece are removed and the back of the objective observed, when it will be seen illuminated by the white card. Pencil marks may then be made on the card at A and B, such that they appear to be just on the extreme diameter of the objective, corresponding to the extreme

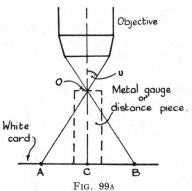

FIG. 99A
Measurement of Numerical Aperture.

rays which enter the lens. By measuring up the distance AB and with the known length of the gauge, then

$$(AB/2)/OC = \tan U$$

from which U may be obtained. Its sine will give the Numerical Aperture of the lens.

(In order to locate the eye when observing the back of the objective, a small cap having a pin-hole in it can be placed over the eyepiece tube. Sometimes a small auxiliary microscope is placed in the draw-tube to enable an enlarged image of the back of the objective to be seen).

This procedure may be used for all dry objectives up to and including a one-sixth inch. Obviously the distance AB could be calibrated in terms of Numerical Aperture and such devices known as card apertometers can be obtained (see Fig. 99b) for this measurement. For immersion objectives it is necessary to have a glass block of known thickness and refractive index (preferably about 1·65). By focusing on the top surface of the block (where an ink mark has been made) and by having lines ruled on the base AC (Fig. 100a), the last ray entering the objective (e.g., from A) may be determined by observation of the back of the objective as mentioned before.

Then from the figure $AC/t = \tan U'$ and U' is related to U by the second law of refraction, namely N'. $\sin U' = N$. $\sin U = $ N.A. Hence, with a knowledge of N' and t, the spacing of the lines along AC could

APERTOMETER DIAGRAM

$\triangle$ = 1 inch.

FIG. 99B
Calibrated Apertometer Card.

again be calibrated in terms of Numerical Aperture. This is the principle utilized in the Abbe apertometer (Fig. 100b).

The following Table V gives a list of objectives and their usual nominal corresponding numerical apertures:—

TABLE V

Focal Length (mm.)	Numerical Aperture.
50	0·12
25	0·20
16	0·27
8	0·55
4	0·85
2	1·25

Resolving Power.

It has been mentioned in Chapter IV that owing to the wave nature of light a lens cannot produce a point image of a point object. Instead it produces a bright spot of light surrounded by one or more diffraction rings, this being known as the Airy disc, and its diameter may be taken as $1·22\lambda/N' \sin U'_m$, where λ is the wavelength of the light concerned N' the refractive index of the medium in the image space, and U'_M the angle that the marginal ray from the lens makes with the axis. If an intensity curve (diagrammatically illustrated in Fig. 101a)

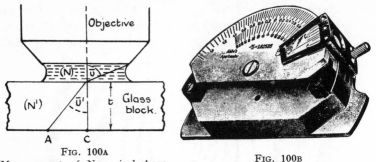

FIG. 100A
Measurement of Numerical Aperture—Immersion Lenses.

FIG. 100B
Abbe Apertometer.

showing the relative illumination of the central spot is drawn for the case when two point objects close together (Fig. 101b) are being observed by the lens, it can be shown that the two images will be separated by a darker region only when their centres are at a distance at least equal to the *radius* of the Airy disc.

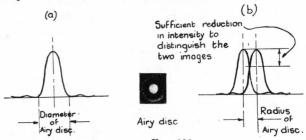

FIG. 101.
Intensity Curves of Airy Disc.

If this physical condition be applied to the case of the microscope, it will be seen how the resolving power of an objective may be deduced. Referring to Fig. 102, the following relation is valid:

$$N.h \sin U = N'.h'. \sin U',$$

where N and N′ are the refractive indices of the media on the object and image sides of the lens respectively, h and h' the respective sizes of object and image, and U and U' the corresponding angles that the marginal rays make with the axis.

In order, therefore, to find the smallest distance between two objects conditional with resolution, h' must be put equal to the radius of the Airy disc, namely, $0{\cdot}61\lambda/N'. \sin U'_m$.
Then,

$$N.h. \sin U = N' \times \frac{0{\cdot}61\lambda}{N'. \sin U'} \times \sin U'$$

but as the medium N' on the image side is invariably air (of refractive index equal to unity)
h thus becomes equal to

$$\frac{0{\cdot}61\lambda}{N. \sin U}, \text{ or Resolving Power} = 0{\cdot}61\lambda/N.A.$$

Hence, the resolving limit of a microscope objective is directly proportional to the wavelength of the light employed and inversely to the numerical aperture of the lens.

FIG. 102.
Lagrange Relation.

The physical constant $0{\cdot}61$ is a value which is subject to slight alteration, according to individual observation, but the formula given may be relied upon provided, of course, the full angular aperture of the objective is utilized. In cases where the condenser has to be stopped down in order to improve the visibility of the object, the resolution will consequently be reduced.
Table VI gives the theoretical resolving power of a number of objectives calculated for wavelength 5555. A.

TABLE VI

| Focal Length. | N.A. | Resolving Power. | |
		Millimetres.	Lines per Inch (Approx.)
$2''$ or 50 mm.	0·12	0·00282	9,000
$1''$ or 25 mm.	0·20	0·00169	15,000
$\frac{2}{3}''$ or 16 mm.	0·27	0·00125	20,000
$\frac{1}{3}''$ or 8 mm.	0·55	0·00061	41,000
$\frac{1}{6}''$ or 4 mm.	0·75	0·00045	56,000
$\frac{1}{12}''$ or 2 mm.	1·25	0·00027	94,000

Practical Tests.

Practical methods for determining the actual resolving power of a microscope objective consist of qualitative and quantative tests. In the former category natural objects, such as diatoms (having minute striations or dots) are frequently used: for example, *Navicula lyra*, *Pleurosigma angulatum* and *Amplipleura pellucida*, being three which may be employed for testing a 16 mm., 4 mm. and 2 mm. objective respectively.

In the latter case, artificial objects in the form of ruled gratings are sometimes used. In this connection rulings by Grayson may be used, which consists of a slide on which there are bands of rulings varying from 10,000 lines per inch up to 120,000 by steps of 10,000.

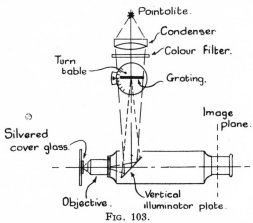

FIG. 103.

Numerical Test for Resolving Power of a Microscope Objective.

Such slides are scarce and difficult to obtain, but an alternative method has been suggested by the author (*Journ. Roy. Micro. Soc.*, 1928, Vol. 48, pp. 144-158), which gives a direct numerical value for the resolving power with a minimum amount of trouble and expense.

This method will be readily understood by referring to Fig. 103. A microscope fitted with a vertical illuminator plate (of good optical quality) is arranged to view a slide on which has been cemented a silvered cover glass. A photographically-made grating (having 600 to 700 lines per inch) is situated at the corresponding conjugate point to the image plane and illuminated by a source of light and con-

(a) FIG. 114. (b)

Comparison Photomicrographs taken in White Light (a) and in Wavelength 3650A (b)—Specimen: Cuticle of Iris Leaf—Magnification = 41 × .

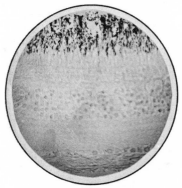

λ = 4500A.

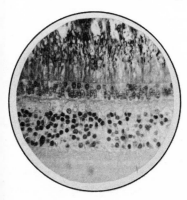
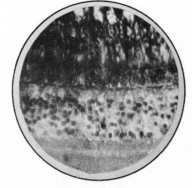

λ = 2749A. FIG. 115. λ = 2313A.

Showing Differential Absorption Effects when using various Ultra-Violet Wavelengths (Specimen: Retina of owl (unstained)—Magnification 450 ×).

To face page 92

densing lens. The objective will then form a reduced image of the grating in the plane of the silvered under-surface of the cover-glass, this image serving as the object for the lens under test. By observing this back-reflected image in the eyepiece the grating is now rotated on its turn-table, when the lines will appear to get closer and closer together until finally they cannot be resolved; at this position the reading on the table circle is taken. If the angle through which the grating has been rotated from the normal is θ and d, the size of the object interval when the grating is at right angles to the optical axis, then the object interval when resolution ceases will be $d. \cos \theta$.

By this means a direct numerical value for the resolving power of a microscope objective can be obtained. The method is a particularly sensitive one, for, by inserting various colour filters, different rotations of the grating will be necessary, thus illustrating that the resolving power increases as the wavelength of the light is reduced.

Relation of Magnification to Resolving Power.

Having determined what is the physical limit of resolution of an objective, it is important to know what magnification is necessary in order to render the resolved object visible to the eye. If we assume the visual acuity of the eye to be one minute of arc, or for more comfortable vision two minutes, then the closest object interval just resolved by the microscope must at least subtend this angle at

the eye, thus the necessary magnification $> \dfrac{\text{Visual acuity limit} \times D_v}{(0\cdot 61\lambda/\text{N.A.})}$

A value between these limits is usually known as " useful magnification." There is no advantage to be gained by further increasing the magnification as no more detail in the object can be made visible to the eye. Should this be done, it is referred to as " empty magnification." We can now, therefore, see what power of eyepiece is required to go with any objective in order to do justice to the resolving power. Table VII gives the necessary magnification and consequent eyepiece power for various objectives.

Photomicrography.

The photography of specimens as seen in the microscope has the advantage of giving a permanent record of the object. It may not have the " elasticity " of visual observation, in as much as change of focus effects are concerned, unless, of course, a number of photographs at different foci are taken. But a photograph can be examined at leisure, and in a detail which may not be possible with an object which is not of a permanent nature.

TABLE VII.

Objective.	N.A.	Necessary Magnification.		Primary Magnification (Nominal)	Eyepiece Required (for 2′ acuity)
		Minimum.	Maximum.		
2″ or 50 mm.	0·12	26 ×	78 ×	3·2	× 16
1″ or 25 mm.	0·20	44 ×	132 ×	6·4	× 14
$\frac{2}{3}$″ or 16 mm.	0·27	60 ×	180 ×	10	× 12
$\frac{1}{3}$″ or 8 mm.	0·55	123 ×	369 ×	20	× 10
$\frac{1}{6}$″ or 4 mm.	0·75	167 ×	501 ×	40	× 8
$\frac{1}{12}$″ or 2 mm.	1·25	280 ×	840 ×	80	× 7

In general, the microscope has to be set up in a similar way and with the same care as for visual work, and then it is only necessary to mount a suitable housing—for carrying the photographic plate—behind the eyepiece, focus the image carefully and expose the plate. It is usually advisable to employ a "projection eyepiece," and the focusing is best done by substituting a piece of clear glass for the ground-glass screen; on the clear glass is an ink line, which may be viewed with a hand magnifier simultaneously with the image of the object.

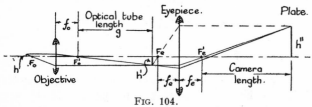

FIG. 104.

Magnification in Photomicrography (Ray Diagram).

A diagrammatic illustration of the image formation in photomicrography and the way in which the magnification may be derived in this case is given in Fig. 104.

Magnification (for photomicrography):

$$= \frac{h''}{h} = \frac{h'}{h} \times \frac{h''}{h'} = \frac{\text{Opt. tube length}}{f_o} \times \frac{\text{camera length}}{f_e}$$

From the diagram it will be seen that, strictly speaking, the "camera length" should be measured from the focal point F'_e of the eyepiece to the plate, but in practice this point is very close to the eyelens, and therefore one can measure from the metal eye-cap without committing any serious error.

As an example of the use of the above formula, let us take a one-sixth inch objective (i.e., $f_o = 4$ mm.) working at a tube-length of 160 mm. and with a × 5 projection eyepiece (i.e., $f_e = 2$ inches), then the primary magnification $m_1 = h'/h = 160/4 = 40$. And if a camera length of 20 inches is to be employed, then

$$m_2 = h''/h' = \frac{\text{camera length}}{f_e} = 20/2 = 10$$

thus giving a total magnification on the plate of 400 diameters. Similarly, if the camera length be made 30 inches in length a final magnification of 600 is obtained, and so on. The correct necessary magnification to employ, however, is given in a later paragraph.

An alternative and advisable method of determining the magnification is to mount a stage micrometer on the microscope and photograph the scale divisions, and then to measure up on the plate the size of a known interval of the object.

Apparatus for Photomicrography.

The general arrangement of the apparatus for photomicrographic work is illustrated in Fig. 105. The illumination system on the left of the diagram consists of a high-power source of light S (such as a " Pointolite " lamp or an automatically-operating arc lamp) and an

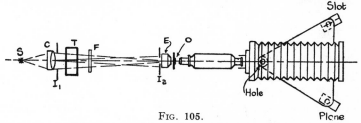

FIG. 105.
Plan view of Photomicrographic Apparatus.

auxiliary condenser C fitted with iris diaphragm I_1. It is sometimes advisable to insert a cooling trough T containing water. The distance of the source and the position of the lens C should be arranged so as to produce an enlarged image of the former of sufficient size to fill the aperture of the substage condenser E. Having focused the object with the microscope, the lens-system E is racked to and fro until an image of the iris diaphragm I_1 is seen in focus in the plane of the object; by adjusting the diameter of this iris the illuminated area of the object is thus controlled.

The iris-diaphragm I_2 should then be adjusted in diameter according to paragraph 6 on page 86. With the projection eyepiece in the microscope, the camera may now be brought into position and set at the correct camera-length, which fulfils the condition of the necessary total magnifying power (see page 97). It is convenient to have the base of the camera arranged with three steel balls, which engage in a plane, slot and hole fitting on the bench (see diagram), thus allowing the camera to be removed and replaced with precise location, so that easy access for the head may be obtained when carrying out preliminary adjustments. After focusing the image in the plane of the plate (as mentioned on page 94) it is helpful to insert a mask three-quarters of an inch wide in front of the dark-slide and take a series of exposures on one plate, changing the fine adjustment by an amount equal to half the depth of focus of the objective. (The depth of focus of an objective can be taken as

$$\frac{\lambda}{4.N.\sin^2 U/2}$$

where U is the angle made by the extreme marginal ray with the axis in the object space; and N the refractive index of the medium on the object side of the lens). In this way the exact focus of the image will be obtained. An appropriate colour filter placed at F (depending on the colour of the object and sensitivity of the photographic plate) will increase the contrast of the final image.

Necessary Magnification in Photomicrography.

The magnification necessary in this case is decided, not by the limitations of the eye (as deduced on page 93), but by those of the grain of the photographic plate. It is, of course, well known that the grain size varies for different types of plate, and measurements show that so-called *fast* plates have an average grain size of approximately 0·02 mm., whilst a *slow* plate (e.g., Process plate) has a size of 0·005 mm. We may therefore take a mean size of 0·01 mm., as a fair measure of the spacing of the silver particles of the average photographic plate used. As, however, the particles are not uniformly distributed over a developed plate, it is considered advisable to arrange the magnification so that the smallest distance between two points in the object should in the image cover at least ten times the grain size, in order to safely resolve the image. Hence the necessary magnification

$$= \frac{0.01 \text{ mm.} \times 10}{\text{object interval resolved by objective.}}$$

Thus, for $\frac{2}{3}''$ objective, magnification $= 0.10/0.00125 = 80 \times$

,, $\frac{1}{6}''$,,   ,   ,, $= 0.10/0.00045 = 220 \times$

,, $\frac{1}{12}''$,,   ,   ,, $= 0.10/0.00027 = 370 \times$

Whilst the above magnifications are sufficient to photographically resolve the image of the smallest object interval discernable by the stated objectives, it may be necessary sometimes to employ twice or three times these figures in order to save enlarging the negative afterwards for the purpose of more comfortable viewing. If, however, shortness of exposure is important, it is advisable to keep to the magnifications set out above.

Illumination of Opaque Objects.

When opaque objects are to be examined with the microscope, the substage illuminator is no longer suitable and other means have to be employed.

Considering first the case of low-power objectives, where the working distance is relatively long (e.g., half an inch or longer), the object may be illuminated by a number of 4-volt lamps suitably arranged at four points round the object glass. (See Fig. 106.) Such a method is also convenient for macrophotography.

With objectives having a focal length of between 25 mm. and 8 mm., and with a working distance down to approximately 3 mm., a "ring illuminator" (Fig. 107) is frequently used. This consists of a parabolic reflector which brings the incident parallel beam to a focus on the specimen; the latter has to be small in dimensions in order to allow the incident beam to pass; but the device is particularly useful, for with the annular illumination thus obtained, all shadows are eliminated.

Another method, which does not, however, necessitate the specimen being small in dimensions, is depicted in Fig. 108. Here the illuminating system is arranged in an outer barrel surrounding the objective and the light is focused down on to the object either by lenticular prisms or a mirror system.

All the foregoing methods have the advantage that the light for illuminating the specimen does not pass *through* the microscope objective, as in the case of the " vertical illuminator " described later. This prevents light being back reflected from the lens surfaces and

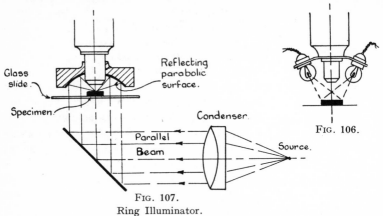

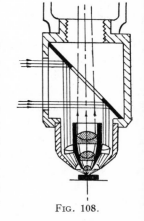

FIG. 106.

FIG. 107.
Ring Illuminator.

causing lack of contrast in the image. This problem of removing back-reflection is a much more serious defect than is generally realized, for in some cases when using metal specimens as the object so much light can be reflected and scattered from the objective that it is not possible to see the surface of the specimen at all.*

Nevertheless, for the highest power micro-scope objectives it is almost essential to use the " vertical illuminator." This consists in its simplest form of a plane glass reflector or right-angled prism (held in an adjustable mount) situated immediately behind the objective (Fig. 109), and thus the incident light is reflected down through the lens on to the specimen. The light returned by reflection at the latter again passes through the objective and through the parallel plate to form the final image. A prism illuminator (see diagram) can also be used.

FIG. 108.

* It is possible that the use of non-reflecting films (see chapter 8) on the surfaces of microscope lenses may help to lessen this trouble.

The arrangement of the optical parts when using a " vertical illuminator " should be given consideration. In order to comply with the condition that the source of light should be focused in the plane of the object, the source or effective source should be situated at a distance from the objective equal to that of the primary image,

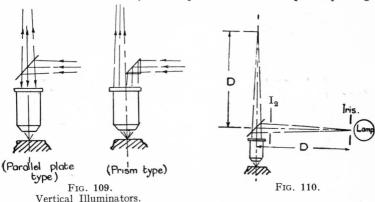

(Parallel plate type)   (Prism type)

FIG. 109.
Vertical Illuminators.

FIG. 110.

that is to say, in Fig. 110 the distances marked D should be similar. Then by having an iris diaphragm in front of the lamp as indicated, the illuminated area on the specimen can be controlled.   *110698*

The distance of this iris from the microscope axis can, however, be reduced by interposing a lens L (Fig. 111) in such a position that a virtual image is formed at the long conjugate of the objective as shown diagrammatically in the figure, thus it is possible to use a short and compact side-tube to contain the vertical illuminator unit. A second iris placed at I_2 (Fig. 110) enables the aperture of the objective to be controlled.

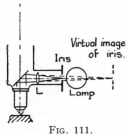

FIG. 111.

When it is necessary to have more light available for illuminating the specimen, such as, for instance, when photographic work is being done with a high-power objective, another arrangement of the optical parts may have to be employed. This is shown in Fig. 112. An image of the iris diaphragm (1) is formed in the plane of the object as before; the source (generally a carbon arc or tungsten arc, e.g., a Pointolite) and condenser L_2 are arranged to give an enlarged image of the former on the lens L_1, which in turn forms an image of the iris (2) on the back lens of the microscope objective. By this means both the aperture of the objective and the illuminated area of the specimen may be controlled, this being done by alteration of the diaphragm (2) and (1) respectively.

Ultra-Violet Microscopy.

The formula governing the resolving power of a microscope objective (namely $0\cdot61\lambda/\text{N.A.}$) indicates that finer detail should be obtained either by increasing the numerical aperture of the lens or by decreas-

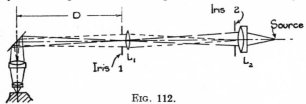

FIG. 112.

ing the wavelength of the light with which it is used. As the upper limit in N.A. has (for some time now) been reached, the only hope of increasing the resolving power is by utilizing shorter wavelengths. Hence, the use of the ultra-violet part of the spectrum in microscopy. A secondary, but nevertheless equally important point connected with such work, is that differential absorption and reflection effects occur in various types of object when illuminated with ultra-violet light

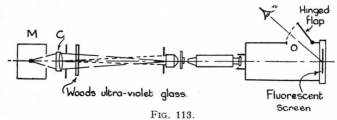

FIG. 113.

Apparatus for Ultra-Violet Microscopy with Wavelength 3650A.

and produce contrasts in the image which are otherwise unobtainable. This is a particularly useful aspect of microscopy, although perhaps not yet fully appreciated; moreover, it is not confined to high power work, but may be utilized in low power work with equal advantage. Even if we go a little way into the ultra-violet these effects begin to show up, and it may be helpful in some work to use a wavelength (such as 3650A), which will still pass through the ordinary glasses without absorption taking place, thus saving the use of quartz lenses such as are required for wavelengths from 3000A to 2000A.

Thus the apparatus shown in Fig. 113 can be quite useful. A well-screened mercury arc M is used as the source of light and an image of this is formed by the condenser C on to the sub-stage illuminator of the microscope, the general set-up being similar to that already described for photomicrography (see page 95). Having focused the object with either an Hg green or violet filter in the illuminating beam, a piece of Wood's U.V. glass (about three-eighths of an inch thick) is substituted for either of these. Such a glass has a maximum transmission at wavelength 3650A and removes the remainder of the visible and ultra-violet parts of the spectrum almost entirely.

In order to focus the U.V. image in the plane of the plate, the ground-glass screen is replaced by an opaque fluorescent screen and the latter viewed from the front by means of an observation window O. The intensity of illumination on this screen will be found sufficient to allow of focusing the image with the microscope, following which a number of photographs on one plate (see page 96) are taken with fine adjustment movements corresponding to half the depth of focus of the objective each time. Such a procedure enables the usual range of glass objectives to be employed, for neither Canada balsam, nor the immersion fluid, absorb at all seriously at this wavelength; there may be some slight spherical aberration introduced by using the lenses at the wavelength for which they are not designed, but it is not sufficient to upset the definition very much. (This may be corrected if desired by alteration of the tube-length).

For initial experiments a biological specimen of some kind will be found interesting as an object, taking one photograph in visual light and one in ultra-violet ($\lambda3650A$). The absorption and contrast effects in the two pictures will in general be quite marked. Fig. 114a and b is an example of this.

U.V. Microscope Using Wavelengths 3000A to 2000A.

In order to further increase the resolving power and contrast effects obtainable with the microscope, it is necessary to use shorter wavelengths than that mentioned in the preceding paragraph. Wavelengths, such as 2749 A, 2313A, 2144A and 1990A, are some of the more prominent ones which have been used, when the resolving power would be increased approximately twice and three times for the first and last named wavelengths respectively. The advantage to be gained when an unstained biological specimen is illuminated with different U.V. wavelengths is clearly shown in Fig. 115, where various stages of absorption can be readily seen.

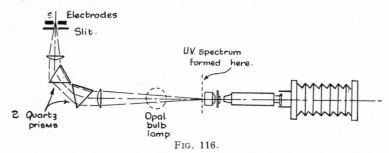

FIG. 116.

Apparatus for Ultra-Violet Microscopy with Wavelength 3000 to 2000A.

In order to carry out such work, however, it is necessary to have the optical parts of the microscope made of some material which will transmit these radiations quite freely. Until quite recently, fused quartz alone has been used for this purpose and the objectives designed for use with individual wavelengths, hence their name "monochromats." With such lenses it is necessary to use strictly monochromatic light, in fact a line spectrum is required to illuminate the object, bringing the line for which the objective is designed on to the substage condenser of the microscope.

Thus the arrangement of the apparatus becomes as illustrated in Fig. 116; a monochromator (having two crystalline quartz prisms, collimator and telescope lens) is shown on the left of the diagram, and provides the means of producing an ultra-violet spectrum from a high intensity U.V. source (such as a spark discharge) in the plane of the substage of the microscope. This spectrum can be made visible by means of a fluorescent screen and by rotating the monochromator as a whole the desired line may be brought into the microscope. It will be understood that the object will have first to be located and focused in visible light by placing an opal bulb lamp in some such position as indicated in the diagram, but when it comes to focusing in ultra-violet light, other means have to be employed. This is carried out by what is, in effect, a fluorescent eye held behind the quartz eyepiece; this device is shown in Fig. 117 and consists of a quartz lens Q with a piece of uranium glass U situated at its focus. Thus the image through the microscope is formed on this screen, which in turn is viewed through a Ramsden eyepiece E having glass lenses. In this way it is possible to find the approximate focus of the U.V. image before commencing to take a series of photographs for finding the exact focus. This latter process is carried out by inserting a mask in front of the plate (as already described) and

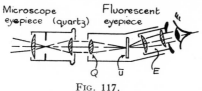

FIG. 117.
Fluorescent Eyepiece.

moving the fine adjustment through an amount equal to half the depth of focus of the objective for each exposure. A fuller description of this whole technique, including the method of producing the spark source, the fluid for U.V. immersion objectives, etc., will be found in Chapter XII of *Practical Microscopy*, Martin and Johnson.

With the advent of new optical materials, it has been found possible to combine lithium fluoride with fused quartz and produce achromatic ultra-violet objectives.* This will, in time, greatly facilitate the methods of ultra-violet microscopy, for with such a lens focusing difficulties disappear and the monochromator may be surplanted by a source used directly in front of the microscope with appropriate U.V. filters.

U.V. Microscope with Wavelengths 2000A to 1000A.

In order to use this range of wavelengths it is necessary to have the instrument in a vacuum; for air (or rather the oxygen content of it) absorbs considerably in this region. The most suitable optical material for use here is lithium fluoride (Li.F.), as this transmits radiations down to 1100A. quite freely, but as there is no material which can be used for achromatizing the lens system, the latter must be of the " monochromat " form and therefore a monochromator must also be employed for illuminating purposes. The arrangement of the apparatus in this case is shown in Fig. 118, in which the entire optical

* B. K. Johnson—*Proc. Phys. Soc.*—Vol. 51—p. 1034—1939.
* B. K. Johnson—*Proc. Phys. Soc.*—Vol. 53—p. 714—1941.

system (made of Li.F.) is enclosed in a metallic vacuum chamber. The spark discharge used as a source is mounted externally and its housing is flushed with nitrogen; this effectively removes the oxygen between the spark gap and the Li.F. window, thus preventing absorption and allowing the spark to operate satisfactorily.

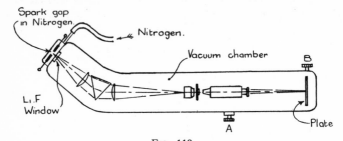

FIG. 118.

Vacuum Microscope for Region 2000 to 1000A—Optical Parts of Lithium Fluoride.

Focusing of the microscope and movement of the plate (for a number of exposures) is carried out by controls A and B through vac.-tight cone fittings. For the metal electrodes at the spark gap, tin will be found suitable, for it gives strong and well-spaced spectrum lines at the following wavelengths*: 1901, 1757, 1640, 1570, 1438, 1347, 1223, 1132, 1062A.

For work in this region it is necessary to use a special form of photographic plate as gelatin absorbs these particular radiations, consequently a Schumann plate, or, better, an Ilford Q2 plate, will be found suitable. It will be obvious that only " dry " objective can be used in a vacuum, and this fact limits the useful numerical aperture of the lithium fluoride lens system to about 0·75; consequently the absolute resolving power of such a microscope used with wavelength 1100A. would not exceed that obtained with an immersion objective (N.A. = 1·25) used with wavelength (say) 2000A. Nevertheless, selective absorption and reflection effects in the object may still be present; this field has to be explored.

Another type of optical system applicable to this work is a form of reflecting microscope. Johnson[1], Linfoot[2] and Burch[3] have all

* B. K. Johnson—*Journ. Scientific Instr.*—Vol. xv., No. 4—p. 126—1938.

[1] B. K. Johnson—*Journ. Scientific Instr.*—Vol. xi, No. 12—p. 384—1934.

[2] *Exhibition catalogue of Physical Society*—Jan., 1939—p. 228.

[3] C. R. Burch—*Nature*—Vol. 152—p. 748—Dec. 25th, 1943.

described methods whereby the objective may consist of a concave mirror accompanied by an auxiliary lens, a Schmidt plate or another mirror.

Let us take a method by Burch depicted in Fig. 119; the objective consists of an ellipsoidal mirror and a spherical convex mirror, with

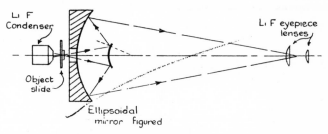

FIG. 119.

A Reflection Microscope suitable for the Vacuum Region.

a hole in the former mirror; this enables the object slide to be placed outside the concave mirror and to be of normal dimensions. By suitable " figuring " of the ellipsoidal mirror such a system can be made free from spherical aberration and coma, although the astigmatism present only allows a small field to be used. The system is, of course, achromatic and if used as an ultra-violet microscope it has the advantage that no change in focus from the visual setting to any desired U.V. wavelength is necessary.

The diagram, from the fact that Li.F. lenses are shown, implies that this type of instrument could be used satisfactorily in the region 2000A. to 1000A., and indeed down to about 300A. provided the Li.F. was removed and a concave grating substituted for use as a monochromator. It must be remembered, however, that the reflecting power of metals[4] decreases very rapidly with a reduction in wavelength and therefore exposure time may be very long.

Electron Microscope.

From what has been said in the foregoing paragraph it becomes apparent that increasing difficulties are met with in the attempt to use shorter and shorter wavelengths with the microscope; moreover, if we go below 300A. we begin to enter the region of X-rays, where it is

[4]B. K. Johnson—*Proc. Phys. Soc.*—Vol. 53—p. 258—1941.

impossible either to reflect or refract the rays, and therefore impossible to form an optical image (as generally understood) of an object.

With, however, an increased knowledge of the behaviour of the electron in its passage *in vacuo* through an electro-magnetic or electrostatic field, it has been found possible to focus a " beam " of electrons and so produce an image by this means.

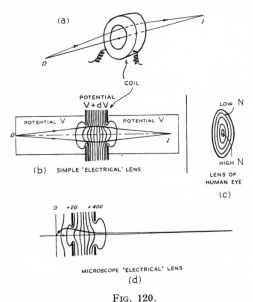

FIG. 120.

For example, if we imagine a stream of electrons emanating from a point 0 (Fig. 120a and b) and passing through the fields of force set up by the coil, the electrons will change their direction of path and " bend " round until they focus at a point I. An " electrical lens " of this kind may be looked upon as being made up of a series of consecutive layers of varying refractive index, much as in the case of the crystalline lens of the human eye (Fig. 120c). If the fields of force are varied in strength by alteration of the potential put through the coils (see Fig. 120d) shorter focus electrical lenses may be produced whose action can be likened to that of a microscope lens.

* L. C. Martin—*Journ. Television. Soc.*—Vol. 1, part 12—p. **377**—December, 1934. V. K. Zworykin—*Journ. Franklin Institute*—Vol. 215, No. 5—p. 535—May, 1933. Busch—*Ann der Physik*—Vol. 81—p. 974—1926.

Although the electron refraction laws* closely resemble those for the refraction of light through glass lenses, the optical analogy is not quite complete, but sufficiently so to enable a study of image formation by electron beams to be made. Electrical lenses, however, suffer from the usual aberrations which are common to optical lenses and have in fact to be used with much more restricted apertures in order to obtain any sort of good quality definition in the image.

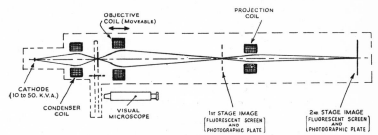

FIG. 121.
Electron Microscope (Diagrammatic).

The wavelength (λ) of an electron radiation may be stated as follows :—

$$\lambda = \sqrt{\frac{150}{V}} \times 10^{-8} \text{ cms.}$$

where V is the voltage applied to the emitting cathode and anode, and the constant 150 being a factor governed by the charge of the electron and its mass (e/m).

If, therefore, we assume a potential V of 15,000 volts we find that the wavelength becomes 0·1 angstrom unit; or fifty thousand times shorter than the wavelength of green light of the visible spectrum. Unfortunately it is not possible at present to have a numerical aperture of the electrical lens exceeding about 0·01, which is approximately one hundred times less than an immersion microscope objective. Nevertheless, by applying the resolving power formula (0·61λ/N.A.) to these conditions, we see that theoretically the fineness of detail resolved should be five hundred times better than with the visual microscope. As yet such a resolving power has not been attained in practice; but only an increase of forty to fifty times that of the visual microscope; in spite of this, however, a very distinct advance has been made and valuable results will, no doubt, accrue from work with the instrument.

A variety of types of electron microscope have been constructed, but their general principle is depicted diagrammatically in Fig. 121, from which it will be seen that the main components (viz., condenser, objective and projection coils) are similar to the optical components in the ordinary microscope, but the whole apparatus is contained

FIG. 122.
Electron Microscope at Royal College of Science, South Kensington.

in a vacuum chamber. The vacuum has to be maintained at a pressure of about 10^{-5} mm. Hg. and as the volume of the container is considerable, this involves experience in vacuum technique and the use of diffusion pumps backed by a fast operating oil pump. Also the maintenance of steadiness in the voltage and current in the electrical lens coils and the electron source is of great importance.

For a more complete description of one form of the instrument, however, reference may be made to the *Journ. Roy. Micro. Soc.*, 1939, Vol. LIX, pp. 203-216, and to *Wissenschaftliche Veröffentlichungen aus den Siemens—Werken*, 1938, Vol. XVII, part I. The

FIG. 123.
Zinc Oxide Smoke Particles × 11,500 (taken with above instrument).

necessary magnification required to resolve the detail given by the electron microscope will obviously be high, and it may be of interest to calculate this for the case mentioned here, namely, when using 15,000 volt electrons, and N.A. = 0·01. The theoretical resolving power would be 6×10^{-7} mm. or $0·006\mu$. If we used a Process Photographic plate (average grain size 0·005 mm.) on which to receive the image, the necessary magnification

$$= \frac{0·005 \times 10}{6 \times 10^{-7}}$$

which is approximately 80,000 times.

If, however, we assume that under present conditions we can only obtain one tenth of the expected resolving power due to the aberrations in the electrical lens, and a consequent reduction of numerical aperture to 0·001 (see page 98, line 21), then a magnification of 8,000 would suffice. In either case such a demand requires that the instrument shall be of rather long dimensions, owing to the fact that the electrical lenses cannot be made of particularly short focal length. A photographic illustration of the instrument is shown in Fig. 122, together with a photograph taken with it of zinc oxide particles at 11,500 times (Fig. 123). Measurement of the diameter of the small spicules indicate that the resolving power here is of the order 0·026μ, that is about ten times better than that obtainable with the visual microscope.

CHAPTER VI

PHOTOGRAPHIC LENSES

In order to appreciate the high quality of definition given by the modern photographic lens, it is desirable to consider what the requirements of the ideal lens are and then to see how nearly such requirements can be fulfilled. An ideal photographic lens should have:—

No chromatic aberration
No spherical aberration
No coma
No astigmatism
No distortion
A perfectly flat field
Rapidity of exposure (i.e. small F/ratio)
Large depth of focus.
Large angular field of view.

It is impossible to design a lens which will satisfy all these conditions simultaneously; and, indeed, it is difficult to correct more than a few of these aberrations at one time. Moreover, as some of the requirements (for example, rapidity of exposure and large depth of focus) are immediately opposed to one another, it is necessary to arrange the design according to the purpose for which the particular lens is to be used.

The meaning of the first four named aberrations have already been explained in Chapter IV, and distortion of the image is a defect which is self-explanatory. Curvature of field, however, requires some explanation.

In Fig. 71 the line foci at A and B are known as the tangential focus and the sagittal focus, whereas the minimum diameter of the constricted rays at C (which is midway between A and B) is known as the disc of least confusion. The locus of these discs as they pass from the centre to the edge of the field is known as the image field; Fig. 124 shows the shape of the latter, together with that of the astigmatic

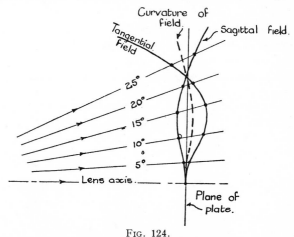

FIG. 124.
Astigmatic Fields of a Photographic Lens.

fields frequently encountered with a photographic lens. The diameter of this disc of light decides the quality of definition given by the photographic lens and should not exceed about 0·003 inches for a plate or print which is to be examined with the unaided eye; but if the negative is to be enlarged afterwards the disc may have to be as small as 0·0003 inch in diameter.

Pinhole.

Although this chapter is devoted to photographic " lenses," one may at the outset make an exception and include the pinhole camera; for although the quality of definition given by this device is not particularly good, practically all the conditions enumerated above, with the exception of short exposure, are automatically satisfied. For example, the absence of distortion, the large (almost infinite) depth of focus, and the large angular field might render the pinhole camera useful in certain cases for photographing architectural subjects where length of exposure does not matter. The most favourable diameter of the hole for a previously determined distance of the photographic plate can be obtained from: —

$$\text{Diameter of hole} = \left(\frac{\sqrt{d}}{120}\right)$$

where d is the distance of the plate from the hole in inches and 120 a factor depending on the diameter of the diffraction disc given by a small hole.

It will be found instructive to take a pinhole photograph with (say) a quarter-plate camera fitted with a properly drilled hole of correct diameter in place of the usual lens. It is of interest to take some pictorial view in which there are both near and distant objects and with wide angular separation; also to take a photograph of the chart shown in Fig. 128 and to compare critically the definition on the plate given in turn by the pinhole and by a well-corrected photographic lens.

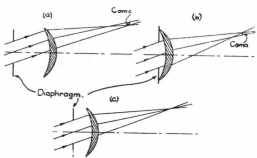

FIG. 125.
Elimination of Coma by Movement of the Diaphragm.

Early Lenses.

The earliest form of lens used in cameras consisted of a bi-convex lens which gave poor results generally. Such a lens had to be reduced in aperture to about F/32 to give any satisfactory definition on the plate.

Wollaston's discovery (1812) for the improvement of definition by using a stop in front of the lens was of great importance; for it can be shown that by moving the stop with respect to the lens a position will be found at which coma can be eliminated. Fig. 125, a, b and c, illustrates this point which can be proved geometrically by means of ray-tracing methods described in Chapter I. This fact is a basic principle utilized in the systematic design of photographic lenses. It can also be shown that a flatter field will be obtained if the lens takes the form of a meniscus shape rather than a bi-convex shape; and in consequence the simple type of landscape lens (as it was then called) was usually as indicated in Fig. 126, c. This type still persists in large numbers in " box " cameras, and although the quality of definition is not good beyond F/16, the small number of air-glass surfaces (i.e., two) prevents reflected and scattered light from reaching the plate and consequently produces good contrast in the image. Hence the popularity of this camera in the hands of the non-technical person.

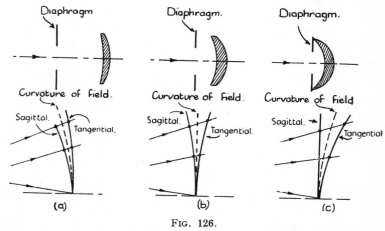

FIG. 126.

Movement of the Astigmatic Surfaces with Change in Shape of the Lens.

An interesting point in the design of this type of lens is that by altering its shape without altering its power or focal length (in other words, by " bending " the lens) the astigmatic surfaces, and therefore the curvature of field, may be changed. For example, in Fig. 126, a, b and c, by making the lens successively more meniscus in shape the curvature of the field can be changed from being curved towards the lens to being curved away from it. The best position of the stop (for the elimination of coma) is shown diagrammatically in each case, and it will be noted that it approaches the lens as the latter becomes more steeply curved. Obviously, then, the design can be arranged such that a flat field and freedom from coma can be secured simultaneously.

Experiment.

An experiment to illustrate some of the foregoing remarks may be carried out as follows: —

Using a short length (about 9 inches) of optical bench (suggested in Fig. 27, mounted in front of some camera bellows) we can place a +5 D lens in its holder and form an image of a page of print on to the ground glass screen. Fig. 127 shows the general arrangement of the apparatus together with approximate dimensions.

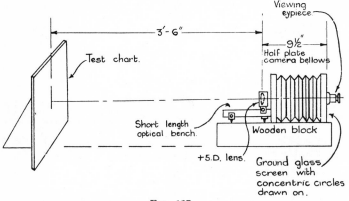

FIG. 127.
Apparatus for illustrating experimentally the principles involved in various types of Photographic Lens.

The object may consist of some good quality printed matter stuck down on to a flat card or board; alternatively an object of the type shown in Fig. 128 can be used. The latter is rather more helpful, as it is designed for the purpose of telling what aberrations are causing the defective image; for instance, the white holes on the black cross will show flared tails when coma is present, the white crosses on black circles will show up astigmatism, the rectilinear lines the distortion, and the asterisks the effects of chromatic and spherical aberration; whilst a measure of the curvature of field may be obtained by racking the ground glass screen from the position of axial focus to marginal focus.

Having set up the object test chart (suitably illuminated) about 3ft. 6in. from the lens, the image is received on the ground glass screen, which has concentric circles drawn on the ground surface. Viewing the latter with an eyepiece, the image may be sharply focused in the centre of the field, the lens being at full aperture (i.e. about one-and-a-quarter inches diameter for a spectacle trial case lens) for the first part of the experiment. By moving the eyepiece outwards

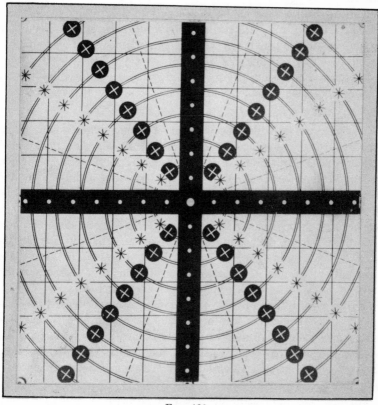

Fig. 128
Test-Chart for Photographic Lenses.

from the centre one can determine when the definition begins to fail and hence (by means of the concentric circles) the diameter of the *good* field. Then place a diaphragm, having a hole of one-half inch diameter, in contact with the front of the lens, and again determine the size of the well-defined field.

Finally slide the diaphragm along the optical bench until there is no sign of coma present, that is when the white holes at the edge of the field show no trace of flared tail on either side of them; this will be the correct position of the stop and observe the diameter of the *good* field. From the diameter of the latter and the known focal length of the lens, the *angular* extent of the field giving good definition mav be obtained; also the ratio of the focal length to the diaphragm diameter will give the F-ratio. These two numerical values are the important factors to know in connection with the performance of all photographic lenses.

(Instead of viewing the ground glass screen with an eyepiece, photographs may be taken and examined critically afterwards.)

Achromatized Meniscus Lenses.

The next stage in the development of photographic lenses was to achromatize the meniscus type mentioned above. At that period (about 1860) photographic plates were chiefly sensitive in the region of the G' line ($\lambda = 4340$.A) of the solar spectrum and therefore the design was so arranged that the D and G' lines were brought to one and the same focus, thus enabling the visual and photographic image to be in the same plane; also, of course, the general definition was improved because of the chromatic correction. The spherical aberration was not entirely corrected, for it is necessary to have some residual outstanding in order to correct the coma (a distinctly worse aberration as far as photographic lenses are concerned).

In the earlier stages of this lens, hard crown and dense flint components were employed; two forms of the achromatized meniscus type are shown in Fig. 129 a and b. Later a third form of this type was evolved (Fig. 129c) using some of the (then) new barium-crown glasses, which enabled a considerable reduction in astigmatism to be obtained.

In order to appreciate the great advance in lens design which occurred when the barium-crown glasses were introduced by Abbe and Schott in 1886, consideration of the Petzval theorem must be made. The Petzval *surface* represents the curvature of field produced by a lens as computed from paraxial formulæ, in the absence of any astigmatism. It is more or less an ideal, for in practice astigmatism is extremely difficult to eliminate; nevertheless the analytical methods of this theorem help considerably in the choice of glasses for the design of photographic lenses.

The radius of curvature R of the Petzval surface for a lens of *small* aperture may be taken as:—

$$\frac{1}{R} = \Sigma\left[\frac{(N'-N)}{r.N.N'}\right]$$

where N and N' are successively the refractive indices of the medium on the left and right respectively of each surface of radius r. For example, if we apply this relation to a single lens (in air) of refractive index 1·52 and with radii r_1 and r_2, then

$$\frac{1}{R} = \left(\frac{N'-N}{r_1.N.N'}\right) + \left(\frac{N'-N}{r_2.N.N'}\right) = \left(\frac{1\cdot52-1\cdot0}{r_1.1\cdot52}\right) + \left(\frac{1\cdot0-1\cdot52}{r_2.1\cdot52}\right)$$

from which it will be seen that in order to make R zero (i.e. to secure a flat field) the radii r_1 and r_2 would have to be equal in numerical value and sign; and consequently the lens would have no power

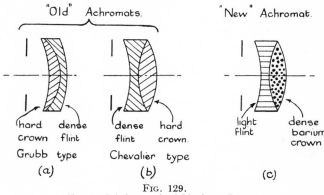

"Old" Achromats.　　　　　"New" Achromat.

hard　dense　　dense　hard　　light　　dense
crown　flint　　flint　crown.　flint　　barium
　　　　　　　　　　　　　　　　　　　crown

Grubb type　　Chevalier type

(a)　　　　　(b)　　　　　(c)

Fig. 129.
Types of Achromatized Meniscus Lenses.

(except due to its thickness) and would in effect be a curved parallel plate. Thus the nearest approach to the fulfilment of the Petzval condition is to have a meniscus lens with radii as nearly similar as the conditions of focal length will allow.

Another way of stating this relation when applied to a single lens is that

$$\frac{1}{R} = \left(\frac{N-1}{N}\right)C$$

where C is the total curvature of the lens, but $C = 1/f.\partial N.v$ where ∂N is the mean dispersion of the glass, v the reciprocal of the dispersive power, and f the focal length of the lens; then

$$\frac{1}{R} = \frac{N-1}{N} \cdot \frac{1}{f.\partial N.v} \text{ or } \frac{1}{f} \quad \frac{v/N}{v}$$

> E.G.   Assuming $f = 10$ inches, $N = 1.520$, and $v = 60.8$,
>
>   then $1/R = \dfrac{1}{10} \cdot \dfrac{40}{60 \cdot 8} = 0.066$, and $\therefore R = 15.2$ *inches.*

When it is required to fulfil the Petzval and achromatism condition simultaneously, as in the case of a cemented achromatic doublet for example, we have

$$\frac{1}{R} = \frac{N_a - 1}{N_a} \cdot C_a + \frac{N_b - 1}{N_b} \cdot C_b$$

where the suffixes a and b refer to first and second components of the doublet, but

$$C_a = 1/f.\dot{\partial}N_a \,(v_a - v_b) \quad \text{and} \quad C_b = -1/f.\partial N_b \,(v_a - v_b)$$

where f is the focal length of the combination so that

$$\frac{1}{R} = \frac{1}{f(v_a - v_b)} \cdot \left[\frac{v_a}{N_a} - \frac{v_b}{N_b} \right]$$

For an achromatic lens with separated components, the condition for zero Petzval curvature is that

$$\frac{1}{R} = \frac{1}{f(v_a - v_b)} \left[\left(\frac{v}{N} \right)_a \cdot (1 - m)^2 - \left(\frac{v}{N} \right)_b \right]$$

where m is the ratio of the separation of the lenses to the focal length of lens a.

From the foregoing it will be seen that in order to secure a flat field the requirements are that the v and N values of the two glasses should rise and fall together. A list of "old" glasses (see below) shows that as the N values rise, the v values fall. This is contrary to the requirements of the Petzval theorem, and a list of "new" glasses (i.e. the barium crown series) illustrates that the drop in v values with a rise in N is very much less. A numerical example will reveal the importance of these so-called "new" glasses, for with them a flatter field and less astigmatism may be obtained.

	"Old" glasses.				"New" glasses.		
	N	v	v/N		N	v	v/N
H.C.	1.5175	60.5	39.9	L.B.C.	1.5407	59.4	38.6
L.F.	1.5427	47.5	30.8	M.B.C.	1.5744	59.4	38.6
D.F.	1.6501	33.6	20.4	D.B.C.	1.6140	56.9	35.2

Let us assume we require a cemented doublet photographic lens of ten inches focal length, and wish to know the Petzval curvature using "old" and "new" glasses; then for "old" glasses:—

	v/N	v
D.F.	20.4	33.6
H.C.	39.9	60.5
Difference =	19.5	26.9

$I/R = 19.5/10 \times 26.9 = 0.0725$
$$\therefore R = 13.8 \text{ inches.}$$

Thus it will be seen that an achromatized doublet using " old " glasses has a greater curvature of field than the ten-inch focus lens of one glass only (see page 118).

Whereas utilizing "new" glasses we have a considerably flatter field (see below).

	v/N	v
L.F.	30.8	47.5
D.B.C.	35.2	56.9
Difference =	4.4	9.4

$I/R = 4.4/10 \times 9.4 = 0.0468$
$$\therefore R = 21.4 \text{ inches.}$$

Furthermore, when using " old " glasses the sagittal field is in most cases nearer to the lens than the tangential field, but the employment of the barium crown glass enables the tangential field to be brought from behind the sagittal field to in front of it, thus giving the possibility of superimposing the two fields (if desired) and eliminating the astigmatism.

An additional point of interest is that if the v/N values were plotted against the v values for all types of glasses (see Fig. 130) we could select two glasses which would give a low Petzval sum by choosing two which gave the least slope of line joining them; for the quantity

$$\left\{ \frac{\dfrac{V_a}{N_a} - \dfrac{V_b}{N_b}}{(V_a - V_b)} \right\}$$

represents the slope of the line joining the two glasses selected and thus for a low Petzval value this slope must be inclined as little as possible towards the horizontal. Thus in the figure the dotted line joining the two sets of glasses indicates that a dense barium crown combined with an extra light flint would give the lowest Petzval curvature.

It will be understood, of course, that the foregoing only gives a general outline of the way in which the Petzval theorem may be utilized for obtaining a choice of glasses when designing a lens system which is required to give a flat field. The theorem, at best, gives a theoretical approximation to the desired aim; and this must always be backed up by exact determination of the aberrations as calculated by ray-tracing methods, nevertheless it is distinctly useful in the initial stages of a design.

Symmetrical Lenses.

It soon became realized that a lens system arranged symmetrically about a central stop is automatically corrected for distortion if object and image distance were the same. Such a lens is also automatically freed from coma and transverse chromatic aberration.

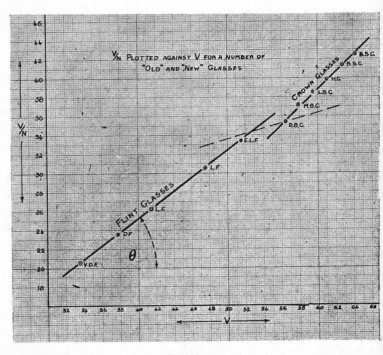

Fig. 130.

Although the correction of these aberrations is only true for unit magnification, they are greatly reduced even when object and image distances are not the same. No advantage is to be gained in axial chromatic aberration, spherical aberration, astigmatism, and curvature of field, by utilizing the " symmetrical principle "; nevertheless, the fact that distortion and coma can be minimized has led to a very great use of this principle.

Fig. 131 shows an early form of this type, which consisted of two meniscus lenses of the same glass with their concave surfaces each facing the diaphragm. The latter had to be greatly reduced in aperture in order to give satisfactory definition; in fact, this lens originally worked at about F/35.

Experiment.

A working model of a symmetrical type lens may be made up with the apparatus suggested in Fig. 127 by utilizing two +2·5 D trial case lenses mounted on the short optical bench, and separated by a distance of 5.7 cm. With the lens system directed towards the illuminated chart (Fig. 128) or page of print, the image may be observed with the eyepiece or photographed on a plate; first with the system at full aperture, and then with a diaphragm of half-inch in diameter placed midway between the two lenses. As before the diameter of the well-defined field can be determined and hence the angular field; also the F/ratio utilized in each case. As the equivalent focal length of this lens system will be similar to that of the single lens on which the first experiments were carried out, a direct comparison in performance can be made.

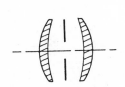

FIG 131.
Symmetrical Type Lens
(Non-Achromatic).

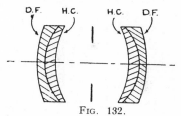

FIG. 132.
Achromatized Symmetrical " Old " Glass
Lens.

" Old Glass " Symmetrical.

Following the simple type illustrated in Fig. 122 it was quite natural that the achromatized form of symmetrical lens would appear, and Fig. 132 shows such a type using the so-called "old" glasses of hard crown and dense flint. This lens was a distinct step forward in the design of photographic lenses, for although the residual astigmatism is still fairly large, the correction of coma and distortion was so much better than had hitherto been obtained, and the additional fact that it could be used at an F/ratio of from 8 up to 5.6 and would still give good definition, led to the adoption of its name as the rapid-rectilinear lens. With this type, however, the astigmatic fields may be swung towards or away from the lens by changing the shape of both components, but the sagittal field is in most cases nearer to the lens than the tangential, just as in the case of the single meniscus or " old glass " achromatized meniscus lens, with a consequent large amount of astigmatism.

" New Glass " Symmetrical.

In order to improve this latter defect it was felt from previous experience that by using two " new glass " achromats as the components, this would be accomplished; but in practice it was found that although the tangential field was brought nearer to the lens it could not be made to coincide with the sagittal field.

Origin of the " Anastigmats."

It was suggested by P. Rudolph (1890) that the symmetrical type lens might be improved by compensating the astigmatism and curvature field given by the first component by an equal and opposite amount given by the second component. This he did by combining an " old glass " achromat as front component with a " new glass " achromat for the rear component (see Fig. 133), at the same time

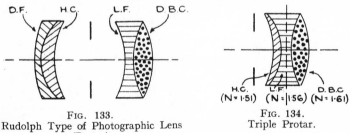

FIG. 133.
Rudolph Type of Photographic Lens
(Protar).

FIG. 134.
Triple Protar.

correcting the other aberrations. This principle led to an excellent design, the definition being good over the entire field of 40 degrees working at an F/ratio of 4·5, the field being particularly flat with relatively little astigmatism.

A series of these lenses were made working at various F/ratios; the lens was originally called the "Anastigmat," but was changed to " Protar " when the word anastigmat became the general term for all lenses having little astigmatism and a flat field.

Rudolph also produced what he called a Triple Protar, which was an attempt to combine an "old" and "new" glass achromat in one compound lens, but using only three glasses instead of four. Fig. 134 depicts this lens and the approximate refractive indices of the glasses are indicated. If we draw an imaginary line through the centre of the middle component, we have what is in effect an "old" glass achromat to the left of the dotted line, and a "new" glass achromat to the right. Such a lens may be used as a single unit (as shown) or as a symmetrical type, in which case a similar combination would be mounted on the other side of the diaphragm.

Other methods of designing an anastigmat involved the use of uncemented components such as for example the Celor type shown in Fig. 135. Whilst the separated lenses of each component allowed an additional degree of freedom in correcting the aberrations, there are a greater number of air-glass surfaces involved and thus a liability to produce less contrast in the image due to reflected and scattered light.

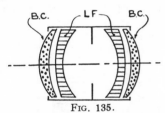

FIG. 135.
Symmetrical Type with Separated
Component.

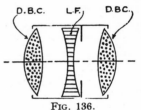

FIG. 136.
Cooke Anastigmat.

Another example of the uncemented anastigmat is the well-known Cooke type (see Fig. 136) originally designed by H. Dennis Taylor. This was an outstanding design and the lens gives excellent definition over a 46-degree field working at F/3·5. There have been various modifications in the construction of this type of lens, such as the Zeiss Tessar and the Aldis anastigmat for example, but the general " Cooke " principle is retained.

Experiment.

A working model of this type of lens may be set up as before employing the apparatus shown in Fig. 127, but using on the optical bench two positive trial case lenses of + 4 D. power separated by 5.8 cm., and a − 3 D. negative lens placed midway between the two. The extent of the well-defined field can be determined either with the eyepiece as explained previously or by taking a photograph, first using the lens system at full aperture and then with a half-inch diameter stop placed as near the negative lens as possible. A comparison in performance can then be made with that given by the model symmetrical lens and also by the single lens.

In these three experiments it will be understood that neither the correct shape of lenses nor the right glasss have been used; nevertheless, the improvement in definition will be plainly noticeable when the successive types are set up; and moreover the general principles thus illustrated in practical form will be found distinctly instructive.

Telephoto Lens.

The purpose of a telephoto lens system is to produce a larger image of a distant object without having to use a lens of undue focal length. The principle will be understood from Fig. 137, in which a positive lens A and a negative lens B separated by a suitable distance d are arranged to receive light from the distant object and form its image

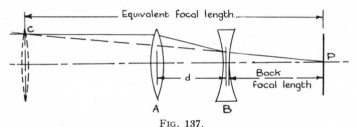

FIG. 137.
Principle of Telephoto Lens.

on the plate P. If now the final direction of the ray leaving the lens B is projected backwards so that it cuts the corresponding incident ray at C, this will be the position of a lens which will have a focal length equivalent to that of the system AB. This equivalent focal length (marked on the diagram) determines the size of the picture, whereas the back focal length (also indicated) decides the camera length. The ratio of the former to the latter, viz. E.F.L./B.F.L., is known as the Telephoto Magnification.

Earlier it was considered desirable to have a telephoto magnification of six or eight times, and this made it difficult to correct the aberrations for a lens working above F/11, but latterly a magnification of two or three times has been adopted. This has led to the design being extended to telephoto lenses now working at F/3.5.

Experiment.

To illustrate the foregoing experimentally, we may utilize the apparatus of Fig. 127 and mount on the optical bench a trial case lens of $+5$ D as lens A (in Fig. 137) and a -3 D as lens B separated by a distance of 10.5 cm. Having received the image of the chart object on the ground glass screen, the distance between two lines in the image can be measured; if the telephoto lens system is now removed and one single positive lens substituted on the optical bench, the right power of lens can be chosen from the trial case which will give the same size of image as that previously measured. The focal length of this lens will correspond to the equivalent focal length of the

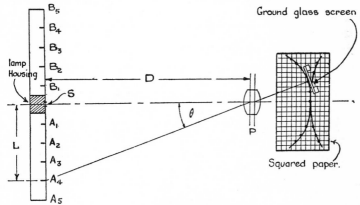

FIG. 138.

Introductory Method for Illustrating and Measuring the Astigmatic Surfaces of a Photographic Lens.

telephoto system. It will be found that a $+3.5$ D. lens will be suitable in this experiment; the distance from the negative lens to the ground glass (i.e. the back focal length) having been measured previously, the telephoto magnification is thus obtained.

Measurement of Astigmatic Fields.

An introductory method of illustrating and measuring the astigmatic surfaces given by a photographic lens may be carried out by the experiment depicted in Fig. 138. A point source S (suitably housed) is set up at about 9 or 10 feet from the lens P and the image received on a ground glass screen which is arranged to stand upright on a piece of graph paper pinned to the table. A vertical line is drawn on the ground glass so that sighting down from above, a point on the graph paper can be marked at the bottom of the line.

The point source is then moved successively to positions A_1, A_2, etc., and in each case the ground glass is moved until the image is focused on the pencil line; and the position marked on the squared paper. As the obliquity of the rays passing through the lens becomes greater, the point image becomes drawn out into two lines at right angles (namely the sagittal and tangential foci). These lines are focused on the pencil line on the ground glass as before, and their positions marked on the graph paper.

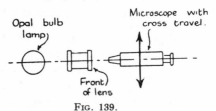

FIG. 139.
Measurement of Entrance-Pupil.

In this way various points on the two astigmatic surfaces can be plotted directly on the paper, and when joined up the shape of the fields may be obtained. Similar points on the other side of the axis can be determined by moving the source to positions B_1, B_2, B_3, etc. The angle of the incident beam for each pair of points can be obtained by measurement of the distances D and L (whence $L/D = \tan \theta$) and should be marked on the paper. It is of interest to carry out this test for a single uncorrected lens and then for a properly designed photographic lens (both of similar focal length) and then to compare the results obtained.

Complete Tests on a Photographic Lens.

1. Focal Length.

The measurement of the equivalent focal length can be carried out by either the magnification method or nodal slide method described in Chapter II.

2. F/Ratio.

It is advisable in certain cases to check the stop numbers engraved on the lens mount for various openings of the iris diaphragm. The aperture-ratio or F/number is the equivalent focal length divided by the *effective* diameter of the diaphragm or stop, that is the " entrance-pupil " of the lens. In order to measure the latter, the lens should be mounted *facing* a low-power microscope having transverse movement (see Fig. 139) and illumination provided at the back of the lens. The iris diaphragm is then focused with the microscope *through* the front lens or lenses and its diameter measured by the travelling microscope. This virtual image of the iris diaphragm is the true entrance-pupil. The process is repeated for the various stop-openings and the different F/ratios thus obtained.

3. Chromatic Aberration.

If the lens is directed towards a distant pinhole illuminated by light from a calibrated monochromator (see Fig. 140 a) the image can be viewed by a microscope having longitudinal movement and the position of the latter recorded for the different coloured foci of known wavelength.

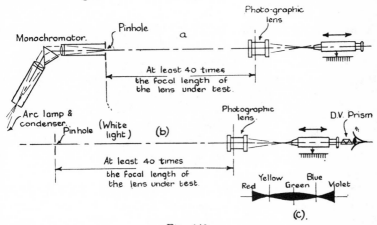

FIG. 140.
Chromatic Aberration Tests.

Alternatively, if the pinhole is illuminated by white light and a direct vision dispersing prism placed behind the microscope eyepiece (see Fig. 140 b), the image of the pinhole will be drawn out into a spectrum which will be constricted at various points (see Fig. 140 c) according to the state of the colour correction of the lens. For example, if the lens was designed to bring the D and G′ line to a common focus, the appearance would be as indicated (c) and by moving the microscope longitudinally each part of the spectrum may be brought to a point focus and the reading off the microscope will give numerical values from which the chromatic aberration against wavelength can be plotted.

4. Spherical Aberration.

This test may be carried out by using the set-up shown in Fig. 140 b, and by judgment of the extra-focal appearances as described in Chapter IV the state of spherical aberration correction may be

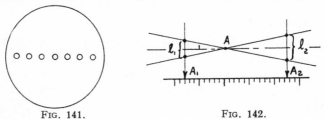

FIG. 141.   FIG. 142.

formed. If a numerical value of the latter is required, a diaphragm having holes at varying apertures of the lens (see Fig. 141) should be placed over the back of the objective and the observing microscope fitted with a scale in the eyepiece. The distance apart of successive pairs of the out-of-focus diffraction discs seen when the microscope is moved through a known distance on each side of the best focus can thus be measured. By knowing the primary magnification of the microscope used, and by employing the Hartmann formula given below, the location of the foci for different zones may be determined and hence the spherical aberration.

In Fig. 142, if A_1 and A_2 are the scale readings of the microscope when the distances apart of the diffraction discs are l_1 and l_2 respectively, then the focusing point A (for the particular zone) from position A_1 will be

$$A = A_1 + \frac{l_1}{l_1 + l_2} \cdot (A_2 - A_1)$$

5. Measurement of Astigmatic Surfaces.

The method under this heading given on page 125 was intended to illustrate the meaning of and to obtain approximate measurement of the astigmatic surfaces; but for more exact determinations of the astigmatism and curvature of field, special apparatus is required.

This consists of a collimator C (Fig. 143), a special form of lens-mounting and an observing microscope M. The lens mount must be able to rotate about a vertical axis, and should have provision for adjusting the lens so that its second nodal point may be arranged to lie immediately over the centre of rotation. The microscope stage S moves in a mechanical slide attached to the lens mount and thus ensures the maintenance of the cross-webs on the stage to be in a position corresponding to that of the flat photographic plate, for whatever angular swing may be given to the lens.

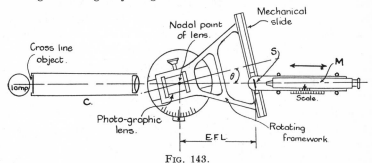

FIG. 143.
Plan View (Diagrammatic) of Photographic Lens Bench for Testing the Shape of the Astigmatic Fields.

In order to measure the amount of astigmatism numerically, the lens is swung into successive angular positions and the microscope M is focused on the vertical and horizontal line images given by the photographic lens, their positions being recorded on the microscope scale. The difference in the readings multiplied by the cosine of the angle θ through which the lens has to be moved will give the true astigmatism. The position of the tangential and sagittal foci with respect to the flat plate (i.e. the reading given on the microscope scale when focused on the cross-webs on the stage) will of course be simultaneously obtained, and these can be plotted as indicated in Fig. 124.

Test by Photography.

Apart from the numerical tests on the individual aberrations given in the preceding paragraphs 1 to 5, it is often helpful in judging the performance of a lens to take a photograph of the chart shown in Fig. 128. But in this case it is advisable to make the chart about 10 to 12 feet square and have it painted on a white flat wall illuminated by daylight. Such dimensions of the chart allow of all photographic lenses between 4 and 10 inches focal length to be tested conditional with the fact that the object distance should be not less than forty times the focal length of the lens. This latter stipulation is based on the fact that the lens aberrations are not seriously affected by utilizing such an object distance.

When such a photograph has been taken, the negative or a print therefrom can be examined for the following defects:—

Aberration.	**Indication given by test chart.**
Coma.	Flared edges to the round white holes.
Distortion.	Lack of straightness of the rectangular lines.
Astigmatism.	The lines of the white crosses on the black circles may appear in focus in one meridian, and out of focus in the other.
Curvature of Field.	The concentric circles may get less well-defined as the edge of the field is approached.
Chromatic and Spherical Aberration.	Poor definition of the asterisk marks and general lack of contrast over the whole picture.

Resolving Power of Lens and Grain Size of Plate.

Whilst the resolving power angle θ of a lens system designed for incident parallel light is given by $1 \cdot 22\lambda/A$ (see Fig. 144) the resolution limit as set by a photographic lens is decided both by the radius of the Airy disc (see page 66) and the ability of the photographic emulsion to resolve this distance. Now the radius of the Airy disc is equal to $0 \cdot 61 . \lambda/N'$. $\sin U'_M$, and taking for example a photographic

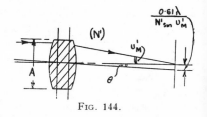

FIG. 144.

lens working at $F/4$ we find that the theoretical radius of the Airy disc is $0 \cdot 0025$ mm.

The average grain size of a developed photographic plate varies from 0.005 mm. for a "slow" plate to about 0.02 mm. for "fast" plates, but since the silver granules are seldom arranged in regular spacings it is necessary to multiply these sizes by a factor of (say) ten in order to *safely* resolve the photographic image. Consequently it can be seen that the photographic plate does not allow the full theoretical resolving power of the lens to be attained; in fact the grain size is about twenty times too large.

More recent fine-grained emulsions, however, such as are used for microfilm work and special micröphotography processes, have a grain size of 0.0005 mm.; but even so, this (allowing for the application of the safety factor of ten) is still twice too large to accommodate the

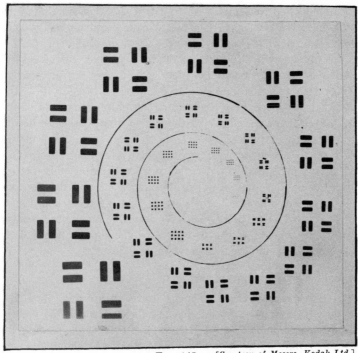

FIG. 145.   [*Courtesy of Messrs. Kodak Ltd.*]
Cobb Chart for Tests on Photographic Lenses.

theoretical resolving power of the lens used at F/4. Nevertheless it will be realized that such recent emulsions are a distinct advance in attempts to obtain the ideal condition of a photographic plate doing full justice to the lens.

Practical Tests.

To carry out a numerical test on the resolving power of a photographic lens it is convenient to utilize a darkened corridor with the lens and camera mounted at one end, and the test object (suitably illuminated) at the other. The latter may consist of alternate opaque and transparent stripes similar to that described on page 57 and the grating rotated through a known angular amount for a number of successive exposures. In this way a position of the grating will be found when resolution ceases, and the line separation of the object corresponding to this can be determined by multiplying the line separation (when the grating is normal to the axis) by the cosine of the angle through which it has been rotated, and hence the angle θ in Fig. 144. It is advisable to use the finest grain plate available for the test, for example Kodak's maximum resolution emulsion, and to have a mask in the camera (as suggested on page 96) so as to allow of several exposures to be made on one plate.

Alternatively, one can use a type of object due to Cobb (see Fig. 145) which consists of a pattern of four pairs of lines becoming increasingly smaller towards the centre.* By photographing the whole object on to one plate one can immediately tell by observation of the latter when resolution ceases, and by locating this particular pattern-set on the original object its dimensions and the distance of the camera lens will give the resolution angle θ indicated in Fig. 144. For an object distance of (say) 50 feet the maximum separation between the centres of the two lines requires to be about 6 mm., going down to a minimum separation of 0.20 mm.

Depth of Focus (Image Space).

The depth of focus in the image space given by a photographic lens may be considered as the distance through which the plate may be moved without causing deterioration of the image (see Fig. 146). In photographic work the criterion of good or bad definition is the size of the blurred patch or disc of least confusion which the eye can detect at normal viewing distance (i.e., ten inches). Assuming the visual acuity of the eye as one minute of arc, the diameter x of the just discernable image patch of a point object would be $x/10'' = 1' = 0.0003$ radians and therefore $x = 0.003$ inches.

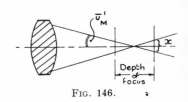

FIG. 146.

* E. W. H. Selwyn and J. L. Tearle (1946), *Proc. Physical Soc.*, Vol. 58, pp. 493-524.

So that half the depth of focus $=0.0015/\tan U'_M$, and for a lens working at (say) F/6, the total depth of focus will be 0.036 inches. The photographic plate must therefore be positioned to within this order of accuracy.

If, however, the picture is to be enlarged instead of being viewed with the unaided eye, the patch size x may have to be ten times smaller (i.e. 0.0003 inches) than that stated above; and this will mean that the depth of focus will also be decreased by ten times.

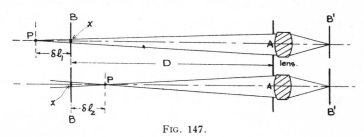

FIG. 147.

Depth of Focus (Object Space).

In Fig. 147, B and B′ are conjugate planes corresponding to object and image respectively for the lens A. Rays from the plane B would pass through a point P on their way to the lens of effective aperture A; hence P is imaged as a patch of diameter x/M, where M is the magnification.

Then $\delta l_1/x = (D+\delta l_1)/A$; $\therefore \delta l_1 = x.D/(A+x)$.

Similarly $\delta l_2/x = (D-\delta l_2)/A$; $\therefore \delta l_2 = x.D/(A-x)$.

Hence the depth of focus $(\delta l_1 + \delta l_2) = (2x.D.A)/(A^2 - x^2)$.

[N.B.—The value of x should not exceed $M \times 0.003''$.]

As a numerical example to illustrate the above, let us assume a lens working at F/6 (i.e. diameter 2″ and focal length 12″) and an object distance of (say) 30 feet.

Then $M = 360''/12'' = 30$ and $x = M \times 0.003 = 0.09$.

And the depth of focus $= (2 \times 0.09 \times 360 \times 2)/(4 - 0.0081)$

$= 32.4$ *inches* or 2 *feet* 8 *inches*.

The Future.

The modern tendency in the design of photographic lenses is to increase the aperture of the lens whilst retaining the same focal length. This appears to be brought about by the increasing demand for light-gathering power and consequent reduction in exposure; such problems as the photography of fast-moving objects, projection work generally (especially in kinematography), and the photography of objects on to 35 mm. film, all demand such requirements. This presents considerable difficulties to the designer and it is only possible at present to remove the undesired aberrations at the expense of cutting down the angular field; for instance, several lenses have appeared working at F/1 but with a total field of only 16 or 18 degrees; nevertheless, with the use of new and recent optical materials, progress in the design of photographic lenses will undoubtedly continue.

The Schmidt Camera.

This device* is an image-forming system for use with a photographic plate and combines features not possessed by a lens system; but whilst it has some disadvantages, it may well prove a solution to many more instrumental problems than those to which it has hitherto been applied.

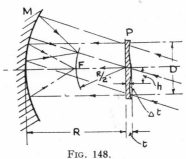

FIG. 148.

Its chief advantage is that it has great light-gathering power, it being possible to use it at an F-ratio of even 0.5. The system is free from spherical aberration and astigmatism, and has extremely small residuals of chromatic aberration; but has one unfortunate drawback, namely that the field is not flat. (The curvature of field is equal to half the radius of the spherical mirror.)

The principle of the instrument is shown in Fig. 148, and consists of a truly spherical mirror M with a circular plate P (situated at the centre of curvature of the mirror) "figured" in such a way as to correct the aberrations inherent with a spherical mirror when used with incident parallel light. The plate or film is situated at the focus

* B. Schmidt, 1931, *Zentztg. Opt. Mech.*, Vol. 52, p. 79.

F of the mirror, and as mentioned before, the field has a curvature of $R/2$. The Schmidt plate P (whether one or both surfaces of it are worked) involves the use of aspherical surfaces, and whilst the optical "figuring" of such surfaces is a difficult operation, the plates can be made quite satisfactorily. Probably the easiest form to make is that shown in the figure in which one surface only is figured; in this particular case the variation in thickness Δt of the plate at any distance h from the axis can be represented by

$$\Delta t = \frac{h^4 - h^2 \ (D/2)^2}{4 \ (N-1) \ R^3}$$

where D is the diameter of the plate and N its refractive index.

The plate may be made in glass or quartz (if required in the U.V. region) and attempts have been made to mould such plates in plastic materials, although it is not yet certain whether the slight instability of these synthetic resins will allow of the accuracy required in this system.

Interferometer Tests on Photographic Lenses.

For those who may be interested in the more advanced methods of testing the performance of photographic lenses by means of the interferometer, the following reference may be found helpful:—
R. Kingslake, *Trans. Opt. Soc.*, 1925, Vol. 27, pp. 94-105.

———————

CHAPTER VII

OPTICAL PROJECTION SYSTEMS.

Projection apparatus may be defined as apparatus in which a source of light is associated with an optical device to produce localised distant illumination.

Light sources may be said to send out light uniformly more or less in all directions, and it is the purpose of the optical system to collect as much of this light as possible and to direct it in the desired direction; so that, for example, a screen may be illuminated by a suitable intensity for comfortable vision (as in the case of the projection of transparent objects) or that a distant object may be brightly illuminated as in the case with searchlights, motor-car head-lights, etc.

As we are therefore interested in gathering as much light as possible from the light source we are immediately concerned with the total *solid cone* of light which can be collected by a given optical system.

The unit of solid angle (sometimes called the Steradian) may be defined as the solid angle of a cone which, having its apex at the centre of a sphere of unit radius, cuts off unit area on the sphere's surface (see Fig. 149).

The value of any solid angle is therefore equal to the area of the sphere's surface included in the angle, divided by the square of the radius of the sphere. Thus, the area of the portion of the sphere's surface shown in the figure $=\pi y^2$; but $y = r \sin U$. So that the solid angle

$$= \frac{\pi r^2 \sin^2 U}{r^2} = \pi \sin^2 U \text{ steradians.}$$

Optical projection apparatus may be applied to a variety of uses, some of which are enumerated below:—

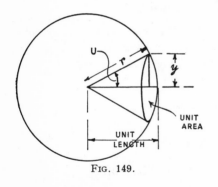

FIG. 149.

(1) the projection of transparencies (such as lantern slides, kinematograph films, etc.).

(2) the projection of opaque objects (i.e. episcopic projection).

(3) searchlights, and headlights.

(4) projection apparatus in industry (for gauge and screw-thread testing).

(5) physical experiments (such as the projection of the spectrum, polarization experiments, interference experiments, etc.).

(6) the projection of minute objects (i.e. the projection microscope).

(7) lighthouse projection systems. (Signal lights, marine lanterns.)

Returning to the case of paragraph (1), one of the simplest (although inefficient) methods of projecting a transparent object on to a screen is to utilize the arrangement depicted in Fig. 150 in which an extended diffuse source of light (such as an opal bulb electric lamp) illuminates the lantern slide S and a suitable lens projects an image of this on to a screen. If such an experiment is tried out in practice, it will be noticed at once that the illumination on the screen is extremely low even at a short projection distance, and moreover its uniformity may not be good and will depend on the evenness of diffusion of the opal glass.

A much more satisfactory method for projection, and indeed the one in most general use, is to employ a high-intensity source of light

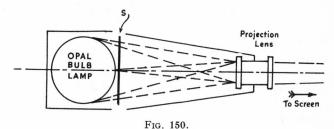

FIG. 150.

and to collect up as large a solid cone of light as possible from the source by means of a lens or/and mirror system, and then to pass all this light through the projection lens on to the screen. The transparent object is placed close to the collecting lens system and is imaged on the screen by means of the projection lens at the desired magnification. In this way much greater intensity of illumination on the screen is obtained, which should be something of the order of five foot-candles for comfortable vision.

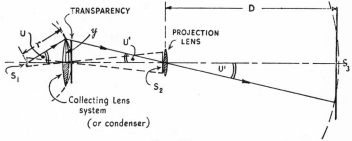

FIG. 151.

Let us look at this system in practice by referring to Fig. 151. The area of the collecting lens or condenser $= \pi y^2$, and as $y = r \cdot \sin U$, this area equals $\pi \cdot r^2 \cdot \sin^2 U$.

Thus, the solid cone of light taken in by the condenser

$$= \frac{\text{area of sphere}}{(\text{radius of sphere})}$$

$$= \frac{\pi r^2 \cdot \sin^2 U}{r^2}$$

$$= \pi \sin^2 U.$$

If B is the intrinsic brightness (i.e. illumination per unit area) of the source and S_1 its area, then the total amount of light received by the condenser $= B \cdot S_1 \cdot \pi \cdot \sin^2 U$.

Now the solid cone of light taken in at the projection lens $= \pi \sin^2 U'$. The intrinsic brightness at S_2 will be $B \cdot t_1$, where t_1 is the transmission factor of the condenser; and if S_2 is the area of the image of the source, then the total amount of light taken in at the projection lens $= B \cdot t_1 \cdot S_2 \cdot \pi \sin^2 U'$.

As the angle of the rays leaving the projection lens will be similar to those entering it, the area S_3 of the screen illuminated at a distance D will be $\pi (D \cdot \sin U')^2$.

So that the amount of light transmitted to the screen will be $(B \cdot t_1 \cdot S_2 \cdot \pi \sin^2 U') t_2$, where t_2 is the transmission factor of the projection lens.

Hence, the illumination on the screen

$$= \frac{B \cdot t_1 t_2 S_2 \pi \sin^2 U'}{\pi \cdot D^2 \cdot \sin^2 U'}$$

$$= \frac{B \cdot S_2 \cdot t_1 t_2}{D^2}$$

Thus, we see that the illumination of the screen is directly proportional to the intrinsic brightness of the source and its area, and in a lesser degree to the transmission factors of the condenser and projection lens (which in most cases will remain constant), whilst it is inversely proportional to the square of the distance D.

A further point, which is evident from the foregoing calculations, and one which is of considerable importance, is the fact that firstly the position and focal length of the collecting lens (or condenser) should be such that as large a solid cone of light as possible may be taken in from the source, and secondly that the *image* of the source should be of such a size that it *completely fills the aperture of the projection lens*.

Sources of Light for Projection Work.

The main essential in projection work is quite obviously a source of high intrinsic brightness. Such sources are in general rather small in area, hence the usual arrangement of conditions as depicted in Fig. 151. For example the carbon arc, which is one of the sources of greatest intrinsic brightness, has an illuminating area (from the positive pole) of about 10 square millimetres (i.e. between 3 and 4 mm. diameter) for a current of approximately 5 amperes. The intrinsic brightness of such an arc is approximately 60 candle-power per square millimetre, giving a total illuminating power of (say) 600 C.P.

With a higher amperage arc, utilizing 40 to 50 amperes (such as might be used in kinematograph projection) the diameter of the (positive pole) crater may be of the order of 7 to 8 mm., with an illumination of 240 C.P. per sq. mm., giving a total of approximately 12,000 C.P.

Whilst in still higher amperage arcs (100 to 150 amps.) for use with searchlights, for example, the crater may be 12 mm. or nearly half an inch in diameter. With such a current density, the intrinsic brightness may be as high as 750 C.P. per sq. mm., giving a total candle-power of 75,000.

However, for the average size of lecture room, the 5 to 10 ampere arc will generally serve as a sufficiently intense source of light, but as its area is still comparatively small (say 4 mm. in diameter) it is necessary to form an enlarged image of this (by means of the condenser) sufficient in size to fill the aperture of the projection system as has already been explained.

It is, of course, well realized that the arc is somewhat unsteady as a source, and this sometimes precludes it from being used for certain physical or optical projection work. One of the more satisfactory sources, as far as steadiness is concerned, is the "Pointolite" lamp (tungsten arc burning in a glass bulb containing argon) generally made in either 100 C.P. or 500 C.P. forms. In the former type the area of the incandescent surface (i.e. a ball 2·5 to 3 mm. in diameter) is about 5 sq. mm., whereas in the latter a glowing plate of 25 sq. mm. is employed. In either case the intrinsic brightness is of the order of 20 and therefore they have only about one third the intensity of the

5 ampere carbon arc. Nevertheless, these lamps are particularly suitable for some kinds of projection work at near distances.

Another form of light-source well suited to projection work is the modern high-pressure mercury vapour lamp. The Hg arc occurs between two electrodes contained in a small diameter silica tube, giving a localized incandescent area of approximately 6 mm. by 3 mm. These lamps also have the advantage of steadiness, but the greater distribution of energy into the green, blue and violet parts of the spectrum may sometimes render them unsuitable for particular forms of projection work; e.g. if projecting coloured transparencies.

They are, however, eminently suitable for certain physical experiments where for example the projection of a line spectrum is desired. One type of this lamp, namely the Mazda ME (250-watts) gives an illumination of 180 C.P. per sq. mm. It runs off 230 volts A.C. in conjunction with a choke and is a convenient compact unit.

Probably the most used form of lamp for the general projection of transparencies, such as lantern slides, film strips, etc., is the tungsten filament electric lamp, in which the filament is wound into extremely small coils arranged closely together, thus giving the effect of a larger area of source than would be otherwise possible with a single straight filament. A range of these lamps is now made with a wattage varying friom 30 to 1,000 watts, taking between 3 and 4 amperes in current. Their intrinsic brightness is of the order of 30 C.P. per sq. mm.

When using these coil filament lamps it is important to remember (as mentioned earlier) that the image of the total area of all the coils should fill the aperture of the projection lens.

Projection of Transparencies.

If we take, first, the more general instruments for projecting a transparent object, such as the lantern slide projector, the enlarger,

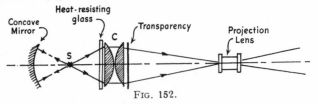

FIG. 152.

or the microfilm reader, the arrangement of the optical system is shown in Fig. 152. The condenser C collects up light from the source S and forms an enlarged image of this of such a size to just fill the aperture of the projection lens. The latter produces an image of the transparency on the screen. If the source is an arc, it is usual to have the positive pole in a horizontal position so that the incandescent crater faces the condenser; if the source should be a Pointolite lamp or coil-filament lamp a spherical mirror may be employed behind the source, so arranged that the source is at the centre of curvature of the mirror thus producing a back-reflected image of the source just to one side of the source proper with a consequent increase in the illuminated area of the source.

The condenser or collecting lens system may consist of two plano-convex lenses as shown in Fig. 152 or of a three-lens device shown in Fig. 153. This latter form can be made to reduce the spherical

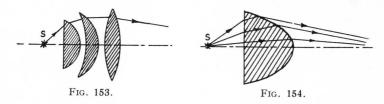

FIG. 153.   FIG. 154.

aberration, and so bring light from all parts of this collecting lens system to a common focus in the plane of the projection lens. For the same reason an aspheric lens may be employed as indicated in Fig. 154. The amount of spherical aberration introduced by the condenser may sometimes be too excessive to be tolerated; for should the marginal rays come to a focus too far from the axial ray focus

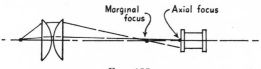

FIG. 155.

(see Fig. 155) the marginal rays may not enter the projection lens and a consequent loss of light on the screen would result. Hence the use of the devices shown in Figs. 153 and 154.

It is desirable in certain cases (for example, when the source is an intensely hot one) to introduce a piece of heat-resisting glass between the source and the condenser (see Fig. 152) in order to prevent damage occurring to the projection lens on which, of course, the heat rays (as well as the light rays) will be focused. Alternatively, one of the condenser lenses may be made of heat-resisting glass. This modern heat-resisting glass has been found to be far more effective in removing the infra-red and heat radiations of the spectrum, than water contained in a transparent cell placed in the beam.

Another arrangement of the optical parts for the illumination of a transparent object particularly when its area is small (e.g. one frame of a kinematograph film) is to form an image of the source directly on to the object (see Fig. 156).

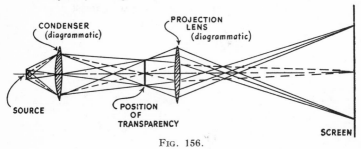

FIG. 156.

A considerably greater intensity of illumination is thus afforded to the object, but greater precautions against the reduction of heat must be attended to, otherwise damage to the object may result. Furthermore, the diameter of the projection lens has usually to be larger in order to take in all the light supplied by the condenser. Moreover, unless the source is uniform in intensity over its whole area (always rather a doubtful condition) the object and hence its image on the screen will suffer accordingly. On account of these drawbacks, this arrangement for projection is possibly not so generally used as the case in which the transparency is placed close against the condenser lens system as shown in Fig. 152.

The Projection Lens.

The projection lens is quite obviously the most important part of the optical system, for on it depends the quality of definition on the screen. It is essential to have the image on the screen free from distortion and a minimum of astigmatism, coma, and spherical and chromatic aberration; at the same time the lens should have as large a light-gathering power as possible, in other words a low aperture-ratio value. (Lenses working at F/3·5 are commonly used.) This immediately imposes stringent requirements on the design of the lens, and good quality anastigmats are therefore the type generally utilized for this purpose. Such well-known lenses as the Cooke, the Aldis, and the somewhat older Petzval are still employed; although manufacturers generally have produced a range of projection lenses of high quality in order to meet modern requirements.

Loss of Light in Projection Systems.

The average efficiency of the ordinary projector system is very low, the amount of light reaching the screen being of the order of 20 per cent. or even less of that from the source. A simple numerical illustration will serve to bring out this point. At each air-glass surface of the lens system there is a loss by reflection of 4 per cent. of the incident light, and approximately a 5 per cent. loss by absorption per centimetre of glass thickness. Thus at the collecting-lens or condenser as much as 30 per cent. may be lost, giving 70 per cent. transmission; at the slide-holder or "gate" 50 per cent. may be lost due to the fact that the "gate" or holder is usually square whereas the condenser is circular in form and must have a diameter sufficiently large to cover the *diagonal* of the transparent object. We have therefore 50 per cent. of 70 per cent. now transmitted, namely 35 per cent. of the initial amount of light from the source. The slide or the film will by surface reflection and absorption probably cause some 15 per cent. loss, which will thus reduce the transmission to 30 per cent.; and finally the projection lens itself will produce a further loss of about 30 per cent., giving a total transmission of 20 per cent. We thus see that only about one-fifth of the incident light from the source will reach the screen.

Furthermore, if a rotating sector should be used in the light path of the projector (as, for example, in the case of the kinematograph) a still further reduction of quite 50 per cent. may result, giving only about 10 per cent. of the initial light to reach the screen.

Illumination on the Screen.

In spite of these considerable losses due to the necessary optical system in projection work it is interesting to gain some information concerning the illumination per unit area on the screen. A further

numerical example will probably serve as the most convenient way
of illustrating this point. For example, let us imagine we want to
project lantern slides in the average size lecture room, and that we
require a picture of (say) 7 feet square on the screen; and further
we will suppose we have available a light source of 1,000 candle-
power.

Now the cone of light taken in by the usual type of condenser
amounts very closely to unit solid angle. Therefore the total light
entering this collecting-lens system will be 1,000 lumens (where the
lumen may be defined as the amount of light emitted in unit solid
angle from a source of 1 C.P.).

We have seen earlier, that in the case of a projection lantern,
approximately only 20 per cent. of the original amount of light gets
through to the screen, that is 200 lumens.

If the screen is to be 7 feet square (namely an area of 50 square
feet approximately) the illumination will be about 4 lumens per
square foot or 4 foot-candles.

This is, as mentioned before, a fairly satisfactory surface illumination for the human eye to view with comfort. In the case of
projection in the cinema, the distance of the screen is considerably
greater than in an ordinary lecture room, and consequently the area
of the screen is required to be larger. A frequent screen area may be
as much as 250 sq. ft. and in order to maintain a surface illumination
of between 4 and 5 ft. candles, a simple calculation will show that the
source of light necessitated is of the order of 12,000 C.P. (e.g. as
obtained from a 40 to 50 ampere carbon arc).

On the other hand, when we come down to the subject of the
projection of microfilm for reading purposes, where the size of the
viewing screen may be only one square foot in area, it follows from
the foregoing numerical illustrations that a source of about 30 to 40
C.P. will suffice. This accounts for the use of even the 36-watt motor
car head-lamp bulb as a satisfactory light source in this kind of work.

For the projection of film strip on to a screen of about two to three
feet square, such as might be used for smaller class rooms; a hundred
or two hundred and fifty candle-power lamp will be found suitable.

Projection of Opaque Objects.

It is frequently necessary and desirable to be able to project opaque
objects on to a screen; especially such things as coloured diagrams and

illustrations, for example. The method for doing this is, in theory simpler than that for projecting transparencies, but in practice it is more difficult. The arrangement of the apparatus required for episcopic projection is depicted diagrammatically in Fig. 157. The

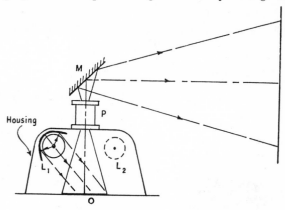

FIG. 157.
Episcopic Projection (diagrammatic).

object O (which for the sake of simplicity let us assume consists of black letters on a white background) is placed in a horizontal position and is illuminated intensely by one or more lamps L_1, L_2. Immediately above the object, a high-aperture good quality anastigmat projection lens P is placed, followed by a surface-silvered plane mirror M arranged at 45° to the vertical axis. The purpose of this mirror is to correct the lateral inversion of the image which would otherwise occur, were the mirror not there.

The lamps and object must be suitably housed, so that no extraneous light gets out into the darkened room; this condition for the removal of stray light is more important in the case of episcopic projection owing to the difficulty of getting sufficient light on to the screen to render the image visible.

In order to gain an idea as to the brightness of the image on the screen given by this form of projection, it may be of interest to make a direct numerical comparison with that given on page 144 for transmitted-light projection. So that, in this case, we will assume that we have a light source of 1,000 C.P. as in the previous example and that the screen image is to be 7 feet square as before.

In the first place, we may treat the illuminated object O as the effective source of light, and consequently we require to know at the outset the intrinsic brightness of the opaque object (assuming that the white portions reflect all the light uniformly).

Let us imagine that the lamp L_1 (Fig. 157) of 1,000 C.P. is situated at one foot from the object O, and the illumination per unit area of the latter will therefore be $\dfrac{1,000}{4\pi r^2}$, where r is 1 ft. in this case.

Hence, the intrinsic brightness of the object

$$= \frac{1,000}{12 \cdot 56} = 80 \text{ candles per sq. ft. (approximately).}$$

Taking the average size of the opaque object to be projected as 10 inches square (i.e. 100 square inches in area), therefore, the effective total candle-power of the object (treated as the light source)

$$= 80 \times \frac{100}{144} = 55 \text{ C.P.}$$

Assuming that the projection lens collects up light of unit solid angle (quite a usual condition) then the amount of light collected $= 55$ lumens.

If one-fifth of the light is lost in passing through the projection lens, the amount of light reaching the screen will be 44 lumens.

As the area of the screen is to be 50 sq. ft., the illumination on

FIG. 158.

Epidiascope (by Messrs. Aldis & Co.).

the screen would be $\dfrac{44}{50} = 0.88$ ft. candles.

Thus, it will be seen that this value is distinctly low when compared with the more general intensity of 4 to 5 foot candles, and in consequence the image would be difficult to see on the screen when viewed from the usual distance.

In order to improve matters, it becomes necessary to increase the brightness of the object, but it will be evident that it must be increased by a factor of something like four to five times. This means introducing additional lamps to illuminate the object; suitable reflectors behind the lamps will also help in bringing more light (theoretically almost double it) to bear on the object. Therefore, in the case quoted here, it might be necessary to fit our episcope with (say) either two 1,000 C.P. lamps or four 500 C.P. lamps (all fitted with reflectors) for the illumination of the opaque object. Naturally, considerable heat will be generated by a group of such lamps, and some instruments are therefore fitted with a fan for cooling purposes.

Manufacturers have also produced instruments whereby (with a slight modification) episcopic projection can be changed to transmitted projection, the combined unit being known as an epidiascope. One type of the latter is shown in Fig. 158.

Sphere Episcope.

The principle of the Ulbricht integrating sphere has been applied to the problem of the projection of opaque objects. Fig. 159 illustrates the principle. A sphere S whose internal surfaces are coated

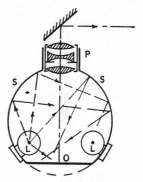

Fig. 159.
Sphere Episcope.

with a high-reflecting matt white paint, is fitted with a high-aperture projection lens P at the top of the sphere, and with an opening at the base for inserting the opaque object O. Lamps are situated at L, and the object is illuminated by the light which has been reflected (perhaps many times) at the internal surfaces of the sphere, also by the direct light from the lamps. Theoretically *all* the light radiated by the lamps should enter the lens P, but in practice light is lost due to absorption at the white surface and also due to the fact that the area occupied by the lens and the lamps will reflect very little. Nevertheless, satisfactory results can be obtained with this device.

Searchlights, Signalling Lamps, Headlights.

The above named are probably the most typical instances of projection apparatus, for it is their function to produce a powerful distant illumination in a predetermined direction.

In these types of device, mirror reflectors are usually employed rather than condenser lenses, as mirrors give freedom from chromatic aberration and involve less loss of light. Moreover if the reflecting surface is of parabolic form, spherical aberration may be eliminated and a much larger "collecting angle" of the light may be secured than with a lens system.

Dealing with the searchlight first, the principle will be understood from Fig. 160 in which a glass surface (ground and polished to parabolic form and coated with a high reflecting metallic layer) is arranged to receive light from the crater of a high intensity arc situated at the focus of the mirror.

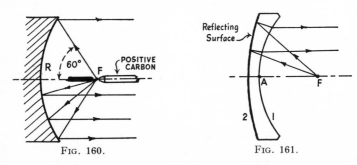

FIG. 160.   FIG. 161.

The well-known property of the parabola, namely that all rays emanating from the focus F will after reflection at the surface emerge parallel to the axis, is the most obvious optical element to employ for the projection of a powerful beam of light; it may be used at an aperture-ratio of between $F/0\cdot5$ and $F/1$ which means (in the former case) a collecting angle of 90°. Unless a hard, tenacious, and heat-resisting metallic coating (such as rhodium) is used on the surface, the heat and fumes from the arc may tarnish it and the surface will lose its reflecting power in a short while. This accounts for some searchlight mirrors being made from a glass disc, both surfaces of which are polished but with the *back* surface silvered (Fig. 161). The thickness of the glass between the silver and the arc thus protects the reflecting surface.

Furthermore, such a lens-mirror can be designed to give freedom from spherical aberration (in other words an emerging parallel beam) by employing two *spherical* surfaces, thus eliminating the difficult process of producing a parabolic surface. Such a mirror (originally due to Mangin) has a radius r_1 of surface (1) equal to the distance of the pole of the surface A from the focus F, and with the radius of the reflecting surface (2) in the ratio of $r_2 : r_1 :: 1.5 : 1$.

Searchlights frequently have a mirror of 5 ft. in diameter, although 3 ft. is the more usual size. The source of light is the crater of the positive pole of an arc running on 50 to 60 volts but with a current of between 100 and 150 amperes. The positive pole is usually cored with cerium and is about three-quarters of an inch in diameter, whilst the negative pole is three-eighths of an inch. The diameter of the incandescent crater is approximately half an inch, and with the above-mentioned current has an intrinsic brightness of about 750 C.P. per square millimetre, giving a total candle-power of 75,000.

Signalling Lamps.

The purpose of a signalling lamp is to direct an intermittent beam of light in a given direction, so that an observer situated in the line of the directed beam may see the flashes (of varying duration) given by the lamp and thus use these as a means of transmitting a message.

The previously mentioned lens-mirror is frequently employed in this device; but instead of the carbon arc being used as a source, a small-area, tightly coiled tungsten filament lamp is quite often employed, more especially with the smaller signalling lamps which may be of from 6 to 10 inches in diameter.

Such electric lamps (about one and a half inches diameter bulb) may have an intrinsic brightness of 24; and as the size of the small coil filament is approximately 2.5 mm. long by 1 mm. wide, the total candle-power would be of the order of 60. The lamp bulbs are sometimes silvered over half their area, the silvered surface being further from the lens-mirror. This not only sends more light to the mirror, but it prevents direct light from the filament going out in the direction of the projected beam which would cause some divergence.

Headlamps.

With a signalling lamp or a searchlight it is generally desirable to limit the projected beam to within small angular amounts; that is, to have almost a strictly parallel beam. But with a headlamp, the requirement is more that of a wide angle beam combined with a central narrow angle of greater intensity than the outer beam. This condition is admirably catered for by utilizing a parabolic reflector in conjunction with a coil-filament electric bulb, but with the latter placed quite close to the base of the parabola (see Fig. 162). As the parabolic surface extends well out in front of the bulb the "angle of collection" is so large that the only light not collected from the source

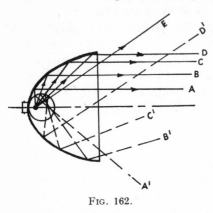

passes out from the front aperture of the lamp to form part of the useful wide-angle beam. In Fig. 162 the rays marked A, B, C and D are those which are regularly reflected at the parabolic surface, and which give the central narrow patch of illumination; whilst E represents one of the rays which go to make up the wide-angle beam. Other rays which help in this latter respect are those marked A',

FIG. 162.

B', C', and D' which have been reflected from the inner surface of the glass bulb and go out in directions indicated in the figure.

Optical Projection for Engineering Purposes.

The checking of mechanical parts such as screw-threads, taps, dies, gear wheels, cutters, gauges, etc., may be carried out with great convenience and rapidity by optical projection methods. Moreover, as the profile of the object is enlarged considerably on the projection screen, small errors may be detected which might otherwise pass unnoticed. If at the same time a master gauge or screw-thread (for example) is projected simultaneously with the gauge or thread to be tested, the instrument can become an admirable form of comparator.

The principle of such optical projection is illustrated in Fig. 163. A source of light S (e.g. a 36-watt coil filament lamp or a 100 C.P. Pointolite lamp) is arranged with a condenser C, so that a *parallel* beam emerges from the latter. The object O (imagined here to be a cylindrical rod shown in plan view) is placed in this beam, and a good quality projection lens P produces an enlarged image of O on to the screen situated at a suitable distance. In the case of usual projection it will be recalled that the distance between the source and the condenser is such that an image of the source is formed in the plane of the projector lens, thus conserving the light collected from the condenser and giving the maximum brightness on the screen. The beam between C and P would thus be *convergent* and the projected image of the object so illuminated tends to show shadow effects with a consequent possibility of incorrect projected sizes on the screen. Unfortunately there is a loss of light on the screen by having an incident parallel beam on the projection lens, but more reliable results will be obtained if this method is adopted. Indeed, it may be necessary sometimes to insert a telecentric stop T in the focal plane of the projection lens to aid in the true projection of the image; this will still

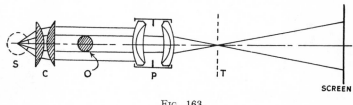

Fig. 163.

further reduce the intensity of the light reaching the screen and a higher power source may have to be employed. This last precaution however is not absolutely necessary in general practice.

It is essential that the projection lens should be a well-corrected one, and especially free from distortion. To this end a "symmetrical" type of lens may be employed or any good quality "anastigmat"; it should be fitted with the usual internal iris diaphragm, for it is frequently necessary to increase the depth of focus of the lens by reducing its aperture, thus enabling such objects as screw-threads, chasers, etc., to be projected without undue out-of-focus effects on the screen.

If the pitch or contour of a screw-thread or a gear-wheel is to be checked by projection, it is necessary first to place a glass scale (divided in millimetres, say) in the plane of the object and to measure the magnification accurately on the screen. (50 times is a convenient magnification to employ.) An enlarged drawing (to this magnification) of the thread or gear tooth is then made on paper and pinned up on the screen, and the projected image arranged to coincide with the line drawing. Discrepancies in manufacture of the screw or gear-wheel will be readily seen by the lack of coincidence between the image and the drawing, and moreover a numerical value of the error may be determined from a knowledge of the magnification.

Various forms of tests and modifications thereof will suggest themselves when the engineer is working with such a piece of apparatus,

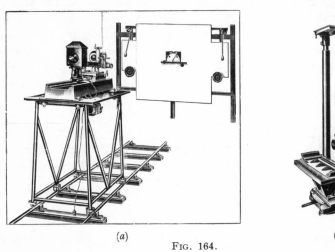

(a)   (b)

FIG. 164.

Engineer's Optical Projection Bench (by The Precision Tool & Instrument Co.)
(a) Horizontal arrangement.   (b) Vertical arrangement.

but these cannot be enumerated here. Fig. 164 shows one form of engineers optical projection bench, by the Precision Tool and Instrument Co. (London).

Projection Work in Physical Experiments.

Numerous occasions occur when demonstrations of principles in physics are required to be shown on a large scale. Optical projection helps very considerably in such illustrations, and the chief unit for such work is a light source of high intrinsic brightness combined with a large-aperture collecting lens (or condenser) suitably housed to prevent extraneous light getting out into the otherwise darkened room. Ample movement between the source and condenser should be available in order to allow for a variation in the vergence of the light leaving the condenser.

Probably the most usual source is the positive crater of a 10 to 15 ampere carbon arc, but the 500 C.P. Pointolite or the 250-watt high pressure mercury arc can also be used. Obviously a great variety of projection experiments may be carried out, and although they cannot all be mentioned here, typical examples of these are set out in detail in *Lecture Experiments in Optics* (B. K. Johnson) published by Arnold and Co. (London). A few of the more generally used demonstrations will, however, be mentioned here. We might take first of all, for example, the projection of the spectrum (illustrated in Fig. 165). A vertical slit is illuminated by an enlarged image of the

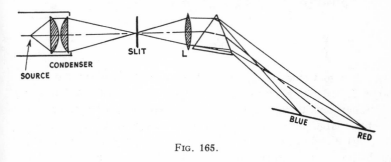

FIG. 165.

source formed by the condenser, the lens L should be of such a focal length and in such a position that when it projects a direct image of the slit on a distant screen, it takes in a similar cone of light to that provided by the condensing lens as shown in the figure. A suitable 60 degree prism, preferably of a high dispersion glass, is then placed immediately after the lens and the spectrum will be formed on a screen some ten or twelve feet away. The lens L need not necessarily be a well-corrected projection lens, but may be a simple lens of one glass only, in which case the screen will have to be inclined in order to maintain the blue and red end of the spectrum in focus simultaneously. This inclination of the screen to the axis has an additional advantage, inasmuch as it increases the length of the spectrum.

Projection with Polarized Light.

The optical projection of ordinary transparent objects is carried out in the manner already described, namely by using a high intensity source S (Fig. 166) a collecting lens C, the object O, and the projection lens L. In order to polarize the incident light before it reaches the object, it is necessary to leave some space between C and O to allow for the interposing of some polarizing device. Undoubtedly the most efficient form of the latter is the Nicol prism but obviously this will have to be of large aperture if we wish to use a large solid cone of light from the source, and placed for example in the position

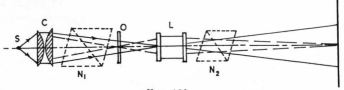

FIG. 166.

N_1. So also would the aperture of the second Nicol N_2 have to be large, in order to allow the full extent of the beam to pass from the projection lens to the screen. As it is extremely difficult nowadays to obtain large pieces of calcite of sufficient size to make Nicol prisms of (say) 3 inches or even 2 inches aperture, one may have to resort to the production of plane polarized light by means of reflection (see page 82 of *Lecture Experiments in Optics*—B. K. Johnson) in which case the aperture is not limited by the size of material available, although the efficiency of this polarizing device is not as good as a Nicol prism. Polaroid plates can also serve as a substitute for the

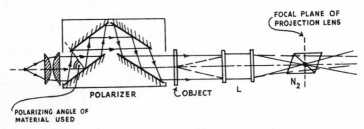

FIG. 167.

Nicol prism, and are now made of quite large diameter, and could therefore be placed in positions N_1 and N_2 shown in Fig. 166. An alernative method is to utilize a parallel beam from the condenser, a polarizer in the form of a reflecting device (see Fig. 167) and a small aperture Nicol prism N_2. Although a loss of light in the projection is incurred by employing a parallel beam (instead of a convergent beam as shown in Fig.166) on to the lens L, this parallel beam will be brought to a focus by the lens in the position indicated and therefore to a much more constricted area than under the conditions shown in Fig. 166. Consequently a much smaller Nicol prism N_2 may be placed at this position and thus allow the full beam to pass to the screen.

Projection of Very Small Objects.

This section may be divided into two headings, one dealing with the projection of small objects covering a comparatively large area (i.e. one inch square) such as the minute lettering on microfilm; and the other dealing with the projection of minute objects of a thousandth of a millimetre or less in size, such as the objects which would normally be viewed with the microscope.

Taking the first case, the arrangement of the optical components is shown in Fig. 168 and as will be seen it is the familiar form of projection system already described, but the important part of this apparatus is the projection lens which is especially designed to cover a wide field (sometimes as large as 60 degrees) and at the same time

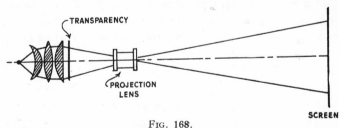

FIG. 168.

working with a low aperture-ratio, frequently F/3·5. As these lenses are often of one inch focal length and their aperture approximately one third of an inch, it follows that the enlarged image of the source falling on the lens must not exceed this dimension and therefore the high intensity source must be particularly small. A very small tightly coiled tungsten filament is frequently employed for this purpose. The design of the condensing lens system also calls for consideration; because this system has to be of exceedingly short focal length and yet it is desirable to pick up as large a solid cone of light as possible from

FIG. 169.

B. K. Microfilm Reader
(manufactured by
Messrs. Wray Ltd.).

the source. Fig. 169 shows one form of microfilm reader. If, however, it is desired to project the image at a considerable distance (say 20 ft.) it may be necessary to use a 5 ampere arc as a source, in which case the condenser lenses should be made of heat-resisting glass. Otherwise the heat of the arc crater concentrated on the projection lens may crack the lenses of the latter.

In the second case, where one is dealing with microscopic objects, it is necessary to use the compound microscope in conjunction with a high intensity source. In Fig. 170 it will be assumed that the microscope has been set up in the usual way (as already described in Chapter 5) and the object properly focussed. At a suitable distance to the left the source (which may be preferably the 250-watt high pressure mercury arc mentioned earlier in this chapter) is arranged with a condensing lens to form an enlarged image of the Hg. arc of sufficient size to fill the aperture of the microscope substage condenser. As the heat concentrated at this point is likely to be considerable, it is advisable to insert a piece or two pieces of heat-resisting glass and

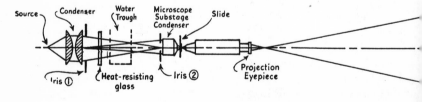

FIG. 170.

possibly a water trough as well, in the beam as indicated in the diagram. This iris diaphragm (marked No. 1) is now the effective source of light, and the microscope substage condenser is adjusted to and fro until an image of this iris is formed in the plane of the object on the microscope slide. Obviously, therefore, the adjustment of iris No. 1 will control the illuminated area on the screen. (The diameter of iris No. 2 controls the effective aperture of the microscope objective as already explained on page 86, where the correct setting-up of the microscope has been given.) It is important to use a special projection eyepiece in the microscope in order to maintain good definition on the screen and to secure a flat field.

With the arrangement described it is possible to project with all powers of microscope objectives including the oil immersion objective, giving in the latter case a magnification of two thousand times for a screen distance of about 4 feet. It is essential, however, to have the room in complete darkness and the light source well housed so that no stray light escapes into the room.

Lighthouse projection systems, Marine lanterns, Railway signal lamps.

The type of projection dealt with under this heading is one in which a strong beam of light is directed in a given direction by means of a lens and prism system rather than by means of a mirror system as in the case of a searchlight or headlight. A mirror is not suitable for this kind of work, for it is frequently necessary to project the light simultaneously in a fore and aft direction, and sometimes (as in the case of the lighthouse lantern) in three or even four directions simultaneously.

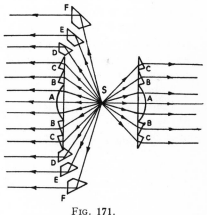

FIG. 171.

Catadioptric Optical System (diagrammatic).

Thus the type of optical system generally employed for this purpose is shown diagrammatically (and in one plane only) in Fig. 171. Referring first to the right hand side of the figure, a lens A is mounted so that the source is at its focus and thus a parallel beam of light emerges from this lens. If now one attempted to collect up a larger solid cone of light from the source by increasing the diameter of this lens, considerable spherical aberration would be introduced and the emerging beam would no longer be parallel. Consequently the beam would suffer a loss in intensity.

In order to overcome this defect, the lens may be kept small in diameter, but circular prisms B and C are arranged concentrically with respect to the lens, and it will be seen from the diagram (which is shown in section only) how wide angle rays from S may be deviated to give an emerging parallel beam of light. A simple device of this kind shining in one direction only is frequently employed for signal lamps on railways; if a similar optical arrangement is used on the other side of the source S, the light beam will be directed in two directions at once. Obviously, three or four such devices may be arranged around the central source, thus representing the state of affairs used with ships' lanterns.

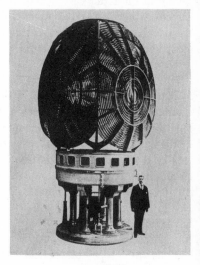

FIG. 172.
Lighthouse "lantern," showing Catadioptric Optical System.

In the case of the lighthouse "lantern" the width of the beam may be extended by employing further circular prisms D, E and F, in which total internal reflection occurs at the hypotenuse face of these prisms and a much greater solid cone of light is thus taken up from the source.

Many lighthouse lanterns are arranged to "flash" at intervals, this being carried out usually by having a number of panels of these catadioptric optical systems arranged around the source and by rotating the whole framework of panels continuously. Each time a panel comes square to the observer's line of vision a "flash" is seen, preceded and followed by a short period of darkness during which the frame is rotating until the next panel comes into position.

The source of light itself must be one of great reliability and steadiness, as well as of high intrinsic brightness. The carbon arc is therefore *not* used, on account of it being defective regarding the first two named qualifications; a 1,000-watt tungsten coil-filament lamp can be used, although the thorium coated mantle heated by an intensely hot flame from petroleum under pressure is still in considerable use. Fig. 172 shows a view of the catadioptric panels used in a lighthouse projection system.

CHAPTER VIII

OPTICAL GLASS: ITS WORKING AND TESTING.

Glass-making has been known since very early times (about **2,500** B.C. in Egypt), but " optical " glass was barely heard of until the second half of the nineteenth century.

A modern glass list, however, may show as many as eighty different varieties of optical glass, and the uninitiated find it difficult to understand why these are necessary. The answer is to be found in the fact that the optical designer is able to produce better and more improved lenses of all kinds if he has a greater selection of glasses to draw on.

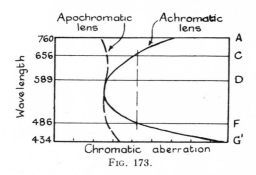

FIG. 173.

A few examples of the advantages to be gained may be quoted:— Firstly, the chromatic aberration of a lens system can be greatly reduced by utilising two or more glasses for its components—see Fig. 173.

Secondly, the spherical aberration and the coma can be corrected simultaneously if suitable pairs of glasses are chosen. In Fig. **174** spherical aberration is plotted as ordinate against various " bendings " of the lens as absicissa, and the familiar parabola is obtained; but by suitable choice of glasses the parabola can be made to move up and down with respect to the horizontal axis. For instance, the spherical aberration curve for a hard crown, combined with a dense flint glass,

crosses the axis at positions where the coma has a considerable positive
or negative value, whereas an objective made from a medium barium
crown, combined with a dense flint, gives a spherical aberration curve
which touches the zero axis almost at the same point as the coma
curve crosses it.

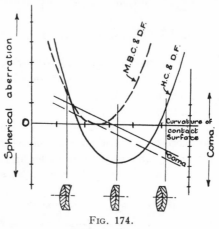

FIG. 174.

Thirdly, the effects of a wide variety of optical glass assists greatly
in the design of photographic lenses, for astigmation can be greatly
reduced and the curvature of field rendered flatter. Introductory
examples showing the way in which this may be brought about have
been shown in Chapter VI.

Fourthly, in microscope objectives of high power the very short
radius of the lens surfaces often introduces zonal spherical aberration
which is extremely difficult to correct. But by choosing glasses with
a large difference of v-value for achromatizing the components, the
curves can be made shallower and the zonal spherical aberration is
less likely to arise. This accounts for the use of such materials as
fluorite (v-value$=95$) being combined with an extra-dense flint glass
(v-value$=33$) to form one or more of the achromatic components in
a microscope objective.

Production of Optical Glass.

The manufacture of optical glass is a highly specialized process and
cannot be compared with the production of other forms of glass, such
as sheet or plate glass, or of " glassware " generally. The reason

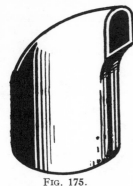

FIG. 175.
Crucible for Production of
Optical Glass.

for this is the high standard of homogeneity and freedom from internal stresses demanded by the needs of optical work. The references given below describe in detail the technique involved in the manufacture of optical glass, but the broad outline is as follows:—

The sand, which constitutes the major content of the melt, must be chosen for its freedom from iron. The other ingredients, such as potassium, calcium, lead, aluminium, barium, boron, etc. (generally in oxide form) are specially selected and mixed with care and thoroughness. The whole is then placed in a dome-shaped crucible or pot with an opening to allow of stirring (see Fig. 175) and raised to a temperature—

FIG. 176.

Glass Manufacture—W. Rosenhain.
Jena Glass—H. Hovestadt.
Dic. of Applied Physics—Vol. 4, p. 82.
Glass—P. Mason.

about 900°C.—until the mass assumes a liquid state. It must be kept in this state until all the " gassing " has ceased and stirred continually until all the bubbles are removed.

On cooling down, the mass of glass thus produced, tends to fracture

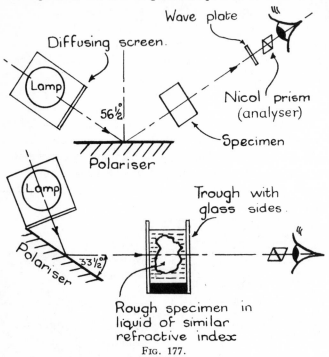

FIG. 177.
Tests for Strain.
Above: Glass Block with Polished End Faces.
Below: Rough Sample of Glass, Unpolished.

and split up into a number of pieces of various sizes (see Fig. 176). These are reheated and pressed into flat slabs, then subsequently examined for freedom from cloudiness, stones, large bubbles, crystallization, etc. The best parts, which often only constitute a quarter of the whole weight, are again re-heated, and this time annealed.

Annealing.

The annealing process consists in cooling the material very slowly through certain ranges of temperature. For the " crown " glasses this is between 500°C and 350°C, whilst with the " lead " glasses the sensitive range is between 400°C and 350°C. This prevents the solidification of the outer parts of the mass whilst the inner portions are still hot, the case which occurs when ordinary cooling is allowed to take place. The latter frequently causes considerable internal stresses to be set up in the glass.

Tests for Strain.

The usual method of inspecting a specimen of glass for strain is to hold it in the path of light in a polariscope (see Fig. 177). The field is made dark by " crossing the Nicols," and the specimen is rotated in its own plane. Strain will be made manifest by the transmission of light in the formerly dark field, and increasing amounts of strain will be indicated by a grey, yellow, red and so on, in accordance with the order of polarization colours given in Table VIII.

A piece of glass which shows no " lighting-up " or even a faint greyness is suitable for most optical purposes; but anything like a bright field or any trace of colour indicates bad annealing and cannot be tolerated.

TABLE VIII.

Order of Polarization Colours.

(Abbreviated.)

Retardation for D-line (microns)	Interference Colours between crossed Nicols	Order
0·00	Black	FIRST
0·10	Lavender-grey	
0·26	White	
0·33	Bright yellow	
0·43	Brownish yellow	
0·54	Red	
0·58	Violet (the sensitive violet)	SECOND
0·66	Blue (sky-blue)	
0·83	Light green	
0·95	Orange	
1·15	Indigo	THIRD
1·33	Sea-green	
1·53	Carmine	

This test may be increased in sensitiveness by mounting a thin plate of bi-refracting material in front of the analyser. The thinness should be such that the retardation is one wavelength for D-light. This produces a violet coloration of the field, and by reference to the table already mentioned it will be seen that a slight change in retardation will produce a marked change in colour. For example, a change of 0.1μ in retardation will give either an orange colour or a bright blue.

Homogeneity.

There may be local regions in the melt where the stirring has not perfectly mixed the material, but has produced *threads* or *striae* similar to those seen when syrup is being mixed in water. Such striae indicate differences in refractive index and may amount to one or two units in the third decimal place.

A method for detecting such defects, as well as bubbles and other small specks of undissolved material, is to place the specimen in the path of a convergent beam of light—see Fig. 178. A large, well-

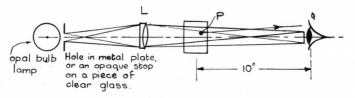

opal bulb lamp

Hole in metal plate, or an opaque stop on a piece of clear glass.

10″

FIG. 178.
Homogeneity Test.

corrected lens, L, forms an image of a small hole or an opaque stop in the plane of the eye. The image diameter should be about 3 to 4 mm. The eye will then see the whole aperture of the lens uniformly filled with light in one case or uniformly dark in the second case. If, then, the specimen, whose faces are polished, is placed about ten inches from the eye, any lack of homogeneity will be revealed by the appearance of either dark or light threads (depending on which method is used) seen in the glass. For if at some point P there is local variation in refractive index from the surround, rays will be deviated from their original path and a change in contrast will be readily observed.

Optical Constants of Glasses.

In order to be able to carry out the design of lenses and optical systems generally it is essential to know the refractive index of the glasses required for a number of wavelengths throughout the spectrum. Those universally adopted are the C-line ($\lambda = 6563$ A. Hydrogen), the D-line ($\lambda = 5893$ A. Sodium) the F-line ($\lambda = 4861$ A. Hydrogen) and the G′-line ($\lambda = 4341$ A. Hydrogen). A glass list also gives other particulars, such as the mean dispersion ($N_F - N_C$), partial dispersion ($N_D - N_C$), ($N_F - N_D$), ($N_{G\prime} - N_F$), and the v-value

$$\left(\frac{N_D - 1}{N_F - N_C} \right)$$

which is the reciprocal of the dispersive power.

Sometimes the ratios of each of the partial dispersions to the mean dispersion are given [e.g.,

$$\left(\frac{N_D - N_C}{N_F - N_C} \right)$$

Numerical values for all the above mentioned quantities are important in optical calculations, and therefore they must be known with accuracy.

They can be measured by making a sixty degree prism of the glass concerned and using a spectrometer for the purpose. Alternatively the Pulfrich refractometer may be used, in which case it is only necessary to polish two faces at right angles on the specimen to be measured. Table IX shows the optical constants of some typical glasses, together with those of some more recent optical materials.[*]

Refractive Index Measurements.

In order to determine the required optical constants of a particular glass it is necessary to measure the refractive indices for the C, D, F and G′ lines of the spectrum. This can be done by employing a spectrometer (Fig. 179) and by making use of the formula

$$N = \frac{\sin\left(\dfrac{A + D}{2} \right)}{\sin A/2}$$

where A is the angle of the prism and D the minimum deviation of the beam (of known wavelength) in passing through the prism. Such measurements entail previous grinding and polishing of two faces of

---

[*] B. K. Johnson—*Proc. Phys. Soc.*—Vol. 55—p. 291—1943.

the glass specimen at approximately 60 degrees to one another, and then in measuring this angle accurately. (See later.)

The sources of light (placed in front of the spectrometer slit) for the minimum deviation measurements may be provided by a sodium

TABLE IX

Material	N_D	Mean Dispersion C to F	V-Value	Partial Dispersion		
				C to D	D to F	F to G'
Fluor crown	1·4785	0·00682	70·2	0·00202	0·00480	0·00363
Boro-silicate crown	1·5087	0·00793	64·1	0·00237	0·00556	0·00445
Zinc crown	1·5149	0·00890	57·9	0·00265	0·00625	0·00506
Hard crown	1·5155	0·00848	60·8	0·00250	0·00598	0·00482
Medium barium crown	1·5837	0·01041	56·1	0·00304	0·00737	0·00596
Dense barium crown	1·6130	0·01025	59·8	0·00302	0·00723	0·00582
Telescope flint	1·5237	0·01003	52·2	0·00295	0·00708	0·00577
Extra light flint	1·5290	0·01026	51·6	0·00300	0·00726	0·00593
Light flint	1·5760	0·01404	41·0	0·00402	0·01002	0·00840
Light barium flint	1·5661	0·01029	55·0	0·00301	0·00728	0·00591
Dense barium flint	1·6059	0·01593	38·0	0·00453	0·01140	0·00967
Dense flint	1·6182	0·01697	36·4	0·00484	0·01213	0·01031
Extra dense flint	1·7566	0·02754	27·5	0·00774	0·01980	0·01736
Fluorite	1·4338	0·00456	95·1	0·00134	0·00322	0·00255
Lithium fluoride	1·3922	0·00370	106·0	0·00160	0·00210	0·00201
Potassium bromide	1·5590	0·01650	33·9	0·00460	0·01190	0·00972
Potassium chloride	1·4901	0·01110	44·1	0·00310	0·00800	0·00631
Potassium iodide	1·6655	0·02840	23·4	0·00860	0·01980	0·01723
Fused magnesium oxide	1·7378	0·01380	53·5	0·00410	0·00970	0·00755
Fused quartz	1·4587	0·00670	68·5	0·00200	0·00470	0·00369
Methyl metha-crylate	1·4881	0·00820	59·5	0·00250	0·00570	0·00540
Trolitul	1·5927	0·01930	30·7	0·00540	0·0139	0·01187

flame for the D-line, and by a hydrogen discharge tube (Fig. 180) for the C, F and G'-lines.

It is possible to measure the optical constants of a glass in a rough and unpolished state*·by immersing the specimen in a liquid of similar

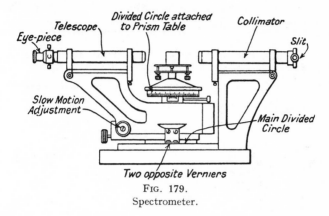

Fig. 179.
Spectrometer.

refractive index contained in a hollow prism (Fig. 181) and carrying out the procedure as above. To do this, however, it is necessary to have a liquid which can be varied in refractive index, and this is

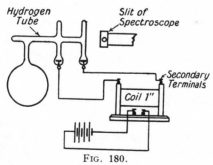

Fig. 180.

usually done by employing two liquids (well mixed), whose relative volumes may be altered very slightly.

Owing to the fact that the liquids frequently utilized for this work (e.g., carbon disulphide, alcohol, benzene, etc.) have a high rate of

---

* L. C. Martin—*Trans. Opt. Soc.*, 1916—Vol. 17—p. 76.
* For the complete setting-up and use of a spectrometer the reader is referred to *Practical Physics* (W. Watson), page 290.

evaporation, the time for which any particular spectrum line will remain sharply defined in the spectrometer telescope is limited, and consequently measurements have to be made rather rapidly and must be repeated several times for reliability; furthermore, in order to keep the two liquids homogeneous it is advisable to have some mechanical stirring device in the hollow prism, but this does not always prove necessary.

In spite of these minor difficulties the method has much to recommend itself, for it is extremely useful to be able to obtain the optical constants of any irregularly shaped piece of glass, of moulded blanks

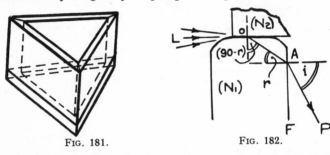

FIG. 181.   FIG. 182.

with greyed surfaces, or of finished lenses which must not be damaged, to quote only a few examples.

Whilst the spectrometer may be looked upon as the fundamental instrument for refractive index measurements, other instruments designed solely for refractometery are employed for measurements on optical glass.   One of these is the Pulfrich refractometer, which is in considerable use by glass manufacturers.

The principle of this type of refractometer will be seen from Fig. 182.   The substance whose refractive index (N_2) is to be measured is placed on the top of a glass block of known refractive index (N_1).   A liquid of refractive index N_1, or slightly higher, may be interposed between the surfaces.   The angle between the vertical and horizontal surfaces of the prism is usually very accurately ninety degrees.   If, then, light enters the material N_2 from a position L, that above LO will enter the Pulfrich prism, whereas that in the direction LO will graze the two surfaces in contact, pass along the direction OA and emerge along AP.   A telescope looking in the direction PA would see a band of light with a sharp boundary line on the upper side.

The angle through which these " grazing " rays have been refracted is $(90° - r)$ and represents the critical angle of the Pulfrich block with respect to the substance above it, and depends solely on the refractive indices of the two materials. The angle, i, at which the beam emerges into the air depends on the magnitude of the angle r, and is measured with the refractometer. Considering the refraction at the two prism faces in turn, we have

$$N_2.\sin 90° = N_1.\sin (90° - r)$$

and

$$\sin i = N_1.\sin r$$

Whence

$$N_2 = \sqrt{N^2_1 - \sin{^2}i.}$$

Tables are supplied with the instrument whereby the refractive index may be determined directly for all values of i.

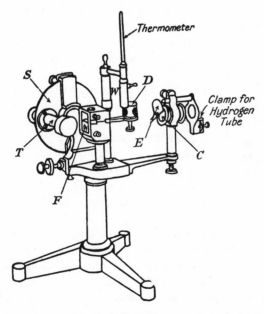

FIG. 183.
Pulfrich Refractometer.

Fig. 183 shows a general view of the refractometer, in which the Pulfrich prism block F, the telescope T and the divided circle S may be seen. The telescope is an auto-collimating one, in order that a back-reflected image of the graticule may be obtained from the prism face F, to give the circle reading for the normal at that surface (i.e., to get the initial zero reading). Readings of the grazing incidence boundary line for the D-line of sodium, the C, F and G′ lines of hydrogen are then taken, and the refractive indices of the specimen for these various wavelengths are obtained from their respective angles, i_D, i_C, i_F and $i_{G′}$.

Glass Working.

Optical glass is supplied either in thick slabs, which have to be cut up along all three dimensions to obtain small plates required for individual lenses, or in thinner plates of approximately the required thickness, which only have to be divided into squares, or finally in pieces moulded to the approximate shape of the lens or prism which is to be made from them. Obviously the last form implies the least amount of preparatory work and therefore appears the most desirable for optical parts which are to be manufactured in large numbers.

However, as slabs of optical glass are still supplied by the glass-maker in large quantities, a word should be said about the dividing-up of such slabs. For pieces up to one quarter of an inch in thickness, the strips or squares may be cut with a diamond or steel-roller glass cutter, tapped on the underside until the cut " splits through," and then breaking off the piece by resting the cut line along a sharp edge of the table, for example.

For thicker slabs, a power hack-saw having a copper blade well supplied with carborundum and water, may be utilised. The glass is held down firmly in position and the copper blade made to traverse the line where the cut is to be made.

Another method is to use a slitting machine; this consists of a round disc about 8 to 10 inches in diameter of soft sheet iron attached to a spindle resembling the headstock of a lathe, the spindle being power-driven and revolving at about 500 to 600 turns per minute. The edge of the slitting disc has small diamond splinters embedded in it and it is due to their presence that the machine is ·capable of cutting quickly through glass and even harder substances. In actual use the lower part of the disc dips into a trough containing a quantity of turpentine or paraffin, so as to keep the whole of the surface in contact with the work wet all the time. The machine usually has some mechanical arrangement for holding and guiding the glass to be cut. Fig. 184 shows such a machine in operation.

The " Roughing " of Lenses.

The second stage in the production of lenses consists in bringing the square plates of approximately the right size and thickness close to the final form of a round lens with the intended curvatures and axial thickness. The first operation is to " shank " or nibble off the

FIG. 185.
Pair of Shanks.

FIG. 184.
Slitting Machine.

FIG 186.

corners of the square plates with a tool known as a " pair of shanks " (see Fig. 185) or to cut them off with a glass cutter and hold them against a revolving stone.

These roughly round plates are then cemented* together by their flat faces so as to form a roll of them (similar to a roll of coins) (Fig. 186). These rolls of blanks are then ground free-hand on a flat revolving tool until the roughness of the edges has been removed and a fairly smooth cylinder of the required diameter has been obtained. In skilled hands this is attained in a surprisingly short time.

The blanks are then uncemented and prepared for grinding the correct curvatures on their surfaces.

---

* A suitable cement is made by mixing equal parts of beeswax and resin, and applying this hot.

For removing the major portion of the glass, special grinding machines (such as, for example, the Adcock and Shipley Grinder) are frequently used, and this process is followed by applying the lens blanks to the proper grinding tools.

The grinding tools, which are generally made of close-grained cast iron, are brought very close to the desired curvature by turning them in a lathe until they fit a metal template of the correct radius; and after grinding convex and concave tools together, they are measured with a dial gauge ring spherometer (described on page 178) to determine whether the finished radius is correct.

The glass blanks are then held with pitch on to one of the tools and this tool is screwed on to the vertical rotating spindle of the machine. The other tool is then placed on top with an abrasive (mixed with water) between the surfaces and whilst the lower tool rotates, the upper one is given an automatic and continuous side-way movement. This grinding process is continued, using successively smaller and smaller grain-sized abrasives, until a fine-ground surface of the glass, free from scratches, is obtained.

The polishing process is carried out by rubbing the fine-ground surface on a pitch lap carrying wet rouge or tin oxide† as a polishing medium. The " polisher " is made by covering the surface of the tool with a layer of melted pitch (suitably tempered in hardness by mixing it with other ingredients such as resin or tallow), which is moulded, as it cools, with the tool of the desired radius. A number of grooves are cut into the pitch lap partly to allow for the removal of debris and partly to retain the rouge paste. Polishing is continued until all signs of " greyness " disappear. The surface should be continually viewed with a hand magnifier to see that no scratches occur during the process.

Principle of the Grinding and Polishing Processes.

Mention has been made of the grinding and polishing machines in which there is one vertical rotating spindle and one moveable arm for producing a reciprocating movement. It is well to understand why these machines take this form, and a very brief treatment of the principles involved in grinding and polishing processes will not be out of place here.

† Cerium oxide is also used.

Let us suppose we have two surfaces in contact with abrasive and water between them (Fig. 187), the lower surface rotating and the upper surface remaining fixed. As each effective grain of abrasive will remove material in proportion to the distance through which it rolls and slides in a given time, and as there are more and more particles on successive circular zones of the discs in proportion to the distance from the centre, it follows that with this arrangement the outer parts of each tool would get worn down more rapidly than the centre parts.

If on the other hand we rub the two surfaces together without any rotation, but with a straight line stroke as indicated in Fig. 188, all the abrasive particles move at the same speed while they are between

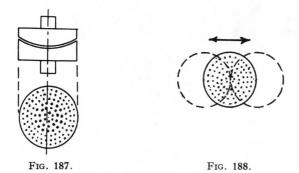

FIG. 187.   FIG. 188.

the surfaces, but they will be in action for different amounts of the total time occupied by the stroke. In the case of the diagram (where the stroke is indicated as being equal to the diameter) only the centres of the discs would be in contact all the time, whereas the extreme edges will undergo grinding only when the moving disc passes through the central position. Without going into greater detail it will be seen that this arrangement tends to produce wearing down of the surfaces in the central parts.

So that, by combining a rotary and a reciprocating movement of the two tools a more uniform wearing down of the whole area of the two surfaces is obtained. These simple facts govern all grinding and polishing processes. It will be realized also that by altering the length of the stroke of the upper tool one can control the radius of the glass work to some extent; for example, by shortening the stroke the wearing down would occur more at the edges of the work and therefore the radius would tend to be made shorter, and vice versa. This control is useful in the finishing stages of a lens surface. Fig. 189 shows a four spindle grinding and polishing machine, the arms B for producing the reciprocating motion are adjusted in stroke-length by a mechanism on the wheel C.

Abrasives.

Hard particles like emery and corundum may act in two entirely different ways when placed between closely fitting surfaces moved

FIG. 189.
Four Spindle Grinding and Polishing Machine.
(Courtesy of Messrs. Bryant, Symons & Co.)

relatively to one another. If they are loose they will tend to roll between the two surfaces; whilst, if they are firmly fixed to one of the surfaces, they will scratch one another and produce a crude form of polish (e.g., emery paper). Under the conditions existing in the optical grinding process we have an intermediate state of affairs, a kind of retarded and intermittent rolling action due to the viscosity of the water with which the abrasive is mixed. For example, if we attempt to grind with loose dry abrasive, there is a grinding action, but progress is extremely slow, due to the fact that only the large grains are rolling forcibly between the moving surfaces, whilst the vast majority roll and slide about idly without producing any effect. Whereas, if a little water is added to the abrasive, then a strongly adherent film forms at both surfaces and practically all the particles come into effective action and consequently the process is greatly speeded up. Hence the reason for the *wet*-grinding process.

For the initial stages of rough grinding, the fastest cutting and most generally used abrasive is carbide of silicon (commercially known as carborundum). The particles (average grain size 0·6 mm.) are hard and sharp, but also brittle, and for this reason do not bear so much pressure as the more robust emery particles. Emery, which is impure aluminium oxide, is used for the successively finer grinding processes in order to bring the glass surface into a state suitable for polishing.

Coarse emeries are graded by passing them through sieves having meshes of from 40 to 80 holes per inch (i.e., grain size decreasing from about 0·6 mm. to 0·3 mm.). The finer emeries are designated as 1 minute, 2 minute, 5 minute, 20 minute and so on up to 100 minutes, these figures being based on the time occupied by the grains in sinking down in a vessel of water one metre high and 30 cm. in diameter. The procedure is to stir up all the emery in the water and then to allow the vessel to stand for the period required (e.g., 20 minutes). The water with the remaining floating emery is then decanted by syphon into a very clean vessel and allowed to stand for two or three days, after which time the water is thrown away and the deposit dried. This would be called the 20-minute emery. The particle size of emeries frequently employed in reaching the final fine-grinding stage are as follows:—

Emery.	Particle Size.
1 minute	0·17 mm.
5 minute	0·07 mm.
20 minute	0·04 mm.
60 minute	0·02 mm.

It will be realized that the regularity of grain size in any one grade of emery is important, otherwise scratching of the glass surface will result, and therefore it is desirable to examine periodically with the microscope (using a magnification of about 100 times) various batches of emery. If a scale is mounted in the eyepiece and the primary magnification has been previously determined, the actual particle size can be measured.

Mention must also be made of Sira abrasive (introduced by the British Scientific Instrument Research Association in 1923), which is a further form of Al_2O_3. This is a fine grained (particle size

$A = 0.083$ mm., Sira $B = 0.028$ mm.) quick cutting abrasive and extremely regular in grain size; it gives a ground surface with shallow pits of even depth and is becoming increasingly used by glass workers.

As polishing may indeed be looked upon as an extension of the abrasive action, it is of interest to note that rouge (Fe_2O_3) the medium generally utilized for polishing processes has a particle size of about 0.005 mm. Sira rouge will also be found to be excellent for optical work.

FIG. 190.
Edging (by hand).

Edging.

When the two surfaces of a lens have been brought to a finished state it is necessary to put on a smoothly ground edge to the lens, and this edge must be concentric with the line joining the centre of curvature of each surface. The process consists in mounting the lens with pitch on to the end of a brass tube (slightly smaller in diameter than that of the finished lens) screwed to a horizontal rotating spindle and then bringing a flat metal plate well charged with wet abrasive slowly to bear against the edge of the glass. Fig. 190 shows the operation in progress as carried out by hand, although there are in most glass shops automatic edging machines.

A word should be said about the initial centring of the lens prior to edging. An illuminated letter T is viewed by reflection at the two surfaces of the lens and the spindle rotated; if the two images seen do not remain stationary the lens is not properly centred, and by keeping the brass tube or chuck slightly warmed the lens can be moved about until this condition is secured.

A fuller and more detailed account of various other processes in the working of optical glass may be found by referring to *Prism and Lens Making*, by F. Twyman (published by Adam Hilger, Ltd., London), *Modern Physical Laboratory Practice*, by J. Strong (published by Blackie and Son, Ltd), pp. 29-92, and the *Dictionary of Applied Physics*, Vol. 4, pp. 326-349.

Testing of Finished Optical Surfaces.

Radius of Curvature Measurements.

When lenses, prisms, flats or mirrors have reached their final polished stage, means must be available for testing the surfaces to see whether they comply with their specified accuracy.

Spherometers.

Dealing with lenses first, it will be realized that the radii of the spherical surfaces which have to be measured will vary from quite short to quite long distances, but a very large majority of surfaces (covering most work) will be from about two inches radius up to about twelve inches radius. For such a range of work the sphero-

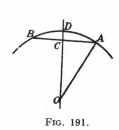

Fig. 191.

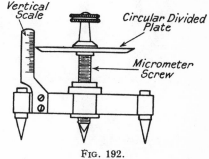

Fig. 192.
Three-Legged Type.

meter is generally employed; this instrument is based on the principle illustrated in Fig. 191, in which BDA is the spherical surface (of radius $OA = r$) resting on a ring whose diameter is BA (i.e., radius $CA = c$).

The distance $CD = h$ is generally measured by means of a micrometer screw, from which the following relation is valid:—

$$r = \frac{c^2 + h^2}{2h}$$

There are various forms of spherometer as shown in Figs. 192 to 196 and whilst they may have defects from a theoretical point of view, it appears better from the point of view of accuracy in readings and consistency in use, to retain the micrometer screw for measuring CD and a parallel-sided hardened cylinder for resting the curved surfaces on. The advantage of the "ring" type of spherometer over the "three-legged '' or '' steel ball '' types, is that the micrometer screw can be positioned much more accurately in the centre of the spherometer circle BA, and further, if the internal or external edges of the hardened steel ring should wear, the sharp edges (and therefore the same internal and external ring dimensions) can be maintained by grinding

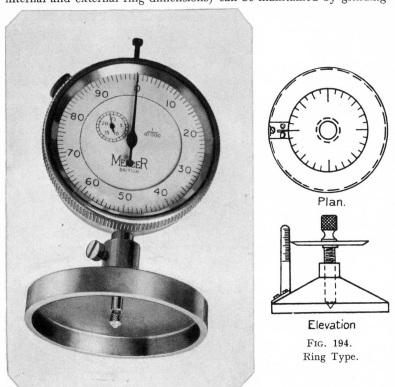

Plan.

Elevation

FIG. 194.
Ring Type.

FIG. 193.
Dial Gauge Type.

off the top of the ring. The difficulty (nearly always experienced) of deciding when the end of the micrometer screw is in precise contact with the surface being measured, may be overcome by utilizing a device shown in Fig. 197, in which the point of contact is observed with a low-power microscope. The appearance seen (Fig. 197a) is that of the steel point or sphere and its image reflected in the surface under test, the micrometer screw being adjusted until the two images just appear to make contact. This is a particularly sensitive setting.

Alternatively a microscope with vertical illuminator is fitted above the surface and the Newton's ring system formed between the surface of the sphere and that of the lens is observed, a method due to Guild.

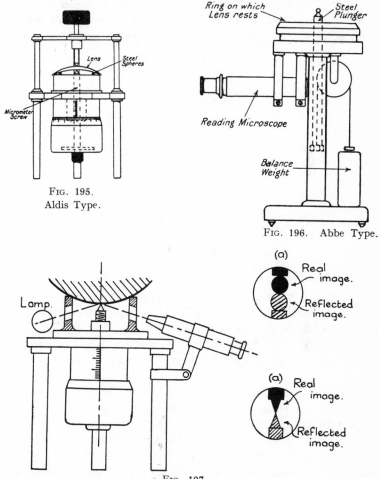

FIG. 195.
Aldis Type.

FIG. 196.   Abbe Type.

FIG. 197.
Method for Detecting Contact between Micrometer Screw and Surface under Test.

Short Radius and Small Diameter Surfaces.

There are many cases, such as eyepiece lenses, microscope lenses, etc., where the diameter is so small that a spherometer could not be used satisfactorily. In order to measure the radius of such lenses an optical method is generally employed similar to that illustrated in Fig. 198. A microscope fitted with a side tube carries an illuminated cross-line C; an image of this is formed by a microscope objective (of about 1 in. or 2 in. focal length), via the plane glass reflector P at the point S_1. If now the concave or convex surface to be tested is

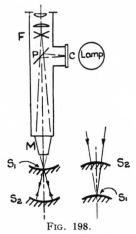

FIG. 198.

placed at this point a back-reflected image of C will be formed in the focal-plane F of the eyepiece. The surface is then moved to a position S_2, such that the rays strike the surface normally when a second image of C will be seen. The distance S_1S_2 (measured by means of a micrometer screw) will give the radius of curvature of the surface.

Two points should be borne in mind when carrying out this test, firstly the back surface of the lens should be smeared with vaseline to prevent any additional reflection therefrom; and, secondly, the objective used should have as small a depth of focus as the working distance and radius of the surface will allow, for this will obviously affect the accuracy of setting with the micrometer screw in any particular case.

Long Radius Surfaces (Concave).

Long radii, such as those met with on the last surface of a telescope objective, for example, or long focus lenses generally (where the radius may be several feet in length) present some difficulty in measurement, because, although the surface may be large enough to allow the spherometer to be used, the accuracy in radius determination is poor on account of the sagitta distance CD (Fig. 191) being very small.

For long concave surfaces a modified form of the Foucault knife-edge method is probably the most suitable. This is depicted in Fig. 199. The surface to be measured is held in a suitable support mounted on a long optical bench, and to the right is a special fitting carrying an illuminated pinhole and a moveable knife-edge mounted

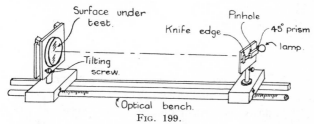

FIG. 199.
Radius of Curvature Measurement by Knife-Edge Method.

in the same vertical plane. Light from the pin-hole is sent up towards the concave surface and is reflected back so that it comes to a focus in the plane of the knife-edge, but the accurate setting of this condition is fulfilled by placing the eye close against the knife-edge and viewing the surface (which should appear wholly illuminated) and then moving the knife-edge slowly across the eye. If, when doing this, the surface darkens uniformly, the knife-edge will be precisely at the focus of the pin-hole and therefore at the centre of the curvature of the surface. The absolute distance between the kinfe-edge and the pole of the surface may be obtained by taking the readings on the optical bench given for the positions of the two mounts and then applying the necessary correction indicated by the use of a rod of known length, one end of which is placed in contact with the surface and the other with the knife-edge. In order to remove back-reflections from the other surface of the lens, vaseline may be applied as mentioned in the previous section.

Long Radius Surfaces (Convex).

The foregoing method cannot be used for convex surfaces, for the image of the pin-hole produced by reflection at the surface would be a virtual one and could not, therefore, be received in the plane of the knife-edge; so that other means have to be employed. One method due to Kohlrausch* is shown in Fig. 200. Two illuminated

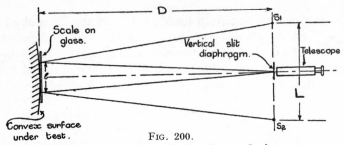

FIG. 200.

Measurement of Long Radius Convex Surfaces.

slits, S_1 and S_2, are viewed reflected in the convex surface by means of a telescope arranged as indicated. The separation of the virtual images of S_1 and S_2 as seen at the surface are measured by placing a glass scale in contact with the former. If l is this distance, L the separation of the real slits, and D the distance (preferably several yards) between the lens surface and the slits, then it can be shown that the radius of the surface

$$r = \frac{2.D.l}{L - 2l}$$

The method is applicable for measurement of concave surfaces also, in which case

$$r = \frac{2.D.l}{L + 2l}$$

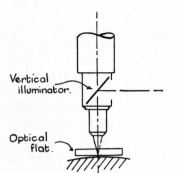

Another method for long radius determination is to utilize the interference fringes (Newton rings) produced when a true optical flat is rested on the curved surface to be measured. By using a measuring microscope fitted with a vertical illuminator (Fig. 201) and employing monochromatic light a large number of rings can be seen and measured. If d_1 and d_2 are the measured diameter of two rings

FIG. 201.

* *Physical Measurements*—F. Kohlrausch, p. 124.

which have $(k-1)$ intermediate rings between them, then the radius of the surface

$$r = \frac{(d^2_2 - d^2_1)}{4k \times \text{wavelength}}$$

Sodium light or the mercury green line may be used, in which case the wavelength will be 0·0005893 mm. or 0·0005461 mm. respectively.

Test Plates.

When lenses are to be produced in large quantities, the testing of the radii of the surfaces is generally carried out by fitting them to a

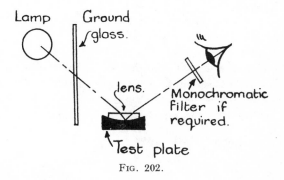

FIG. 202.

master test plate instead of measuring each surface individually by one of the means already mentioned; the latter procedure taking too long for mass production methods.

This consists in making the test plate first (as described later) and then placing the finished surface carefully in contact with the former and observing the interference pattern seen by reflected diffused light (Fig. 202). If the surface (being made) fitted the test plate surface perfectly only one colour would be seen over the whole area of the lens, but more usually a number of circular fringes are seen.

Let us consider what occurs when light is incident on an air film between two glass surfaces (i.e., when the surfaces do not fit exactly). In Fig. 203, OA is an incident ray travelling in glass of refractive index N and meeting the air film of refractive N^1 at A. Part of the light will be reflected along AB and part refracted along AE; the latter ray will be reflected at E and refracted into the glass again at C. It can be easily deduced that the retardation XD between the two portions of the beam is equal to $N'.2t.\cos i'$, where t is the thickness of the air film and i' the angle of refraction. If this retardation is equal to one wavelength or a multiple of a wavelength of the light being used, then a dark interference fringe will be seen on the surface

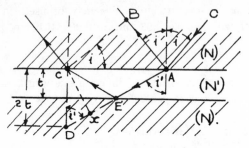

FIG. 203.

at A. (At first it would appear that the difference in path length between AB and AEC should be half a wavelength in order to produce interference, but it must be remembered that there is a phase change of $\lambda/2$ by reflection at the rarer-to-denser medium at the point E).

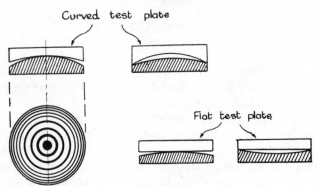

FIG. 204.
Interference Figures with Curved and Flat Test-Plates.

Thus, by looking in the direction BA, any lack of fitting of the surfaces would be indicated by the appearance of alternate light and dark interference fringes, any one fringe corresponding to a constant thickness t of air film throughout the surface; for example, the appearance might be that shown in Fig. 204, which may be looked upon as a contour map of the surface under examination.

In order to determine whether the contact is at the centre or edges of the standard test plate, it is only necessary to move the head so that the angle of incidence of the light on the surfaces is changed. For instance, if we move the head downwards, thus increasing the angle i and therefore i', the quantity $N'.2t.\cos i'$ (giving the retardation for any particular fringe) will be decreased numerically—for as i' increases, the cosine of i' decreases—and therefore for any particular fringe to maintain its original retardation it must move to a region of greater air thickness. So that if the fringes expand from a centre,

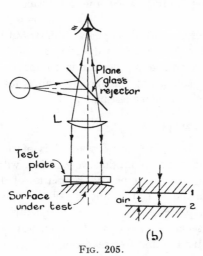

(b)

Fig. 205.

contact in the centre of the test-plate would be indicated, whereas if they contract to a centre there would be contact on the edges. This test is particularly useful when applied to testing a so-called flat surface against a standard optical flat, for obviously one can tell whether the surface being made is relatively convex or concave and the polishing stroke can be arranged to correct this.

Instead of using oblique illumination (shown in Fig. 202) for the examination of the surfaces, sometimes vertical illumination is employed and an instrument known as an interferoscope can be used (Fig. 205). Light from an extended monochromatic source is reflected downward by a plane glass reflector and rendered parallel by a lens L. On returning from the surface under test the light is brought to a focus in the plane of the eye and the interference fringes are seen. For this case where normal incidence of the light is used, the angle i' is ninety degrees and therefore its cosine is unity, so that from the foregoing equation the retardation between the two portions of the beam reflected at surface 1 and 2 (see Fig. 205b) is equal to $\left(2t - \dfrac{\lambda}{2} \right)$ (The $\lambda/2$ represents the phase change by reflection at the denser medium, i.e., at surface 2). Consequently the first dark fringe seen from the centre outwards (e.g., if a flat surface is rested on a convex surface) would occur when $2t =$ wavelength of the light being utilized, in other words, when the air space is equal to half a wavelength.

We may, therefore, with this apparatus draw out the surface under test to scale, mark the position of the fringes; and knowing that each dark fringe corresponds to an increase in air space of $\lambda/2$ a sectional diagram can be made giving the absolute values for the departure of the surface from the standard test-plate.

The Making of Test-plates.

The optical " flat " or " proof plane " is of such importance in the workshop and testing-room that we will deal with this first. The principle is based on the geometrical properties of the plane surface, namely, that the plane is the only possible surface which is self-congruent in all possible positions. Consequently, if we make the surfaces of two separate glass plates to fit accurately the surface of a third plate and try the first two plates on one another; then, if they fit, the three surfaces will be true planes. If they do not fit, they provide means of systematic improvement until a sufficiently close approach to the ideal plane is secured.

The practical procedure is to commence with three circular plates of glass (clearly marked 1, 2 and 3) and to finely grind the surfaces. No. 1 is then sufficiently polished to show Newton's rings and is used as a preliminary standard by which No. 2 and 3 are controlled. No. 2 and 3 are also polished until their surfaces fit No. 1 much more closely (i.e., show fewer rings), than they fit each other. Let us assume that 2 and 3 are found to be convex; we then " figure " them alternately and equally until their fit is greatly improved. We go back to No. 1, which will now show marginal rings when fitted with 2 or 3, and No. 1 is now polished down until the marginal fringes disappear. This process is repeated until each plate begins to show colour when applied to the other two, and then continued until the desired state of perfection (e.g., one colour over the entire area of the plates) has been reached.

Other Methods of Testing a Plane Surface.

A plane surface may be tested by relying on optical principles only; for a plane is the only surface which can produce a perfect image of a luminous point obliquely reflected in it—a spherical surface (however slight) will produce an astigmatic image. Making use of this principle, the test consists in viewing a distant point object (i.e., an artificial star) with a well corrected telescope after the light has been reflected obliquely in the surface under test (see Fig. 206).

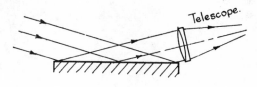

FIG. 206.

By examination of the expanded star-image (i.e., by racking the eyepiece in and out of focus) the state of the surface can be judged. For if the surface has the slightest tendency towards astigmatic form this will be indicated by elliptical expanded images on each side of the best focus; whereas, if the surface is truly plane, circular patches of light will be seen. If the surface is laid in a horizontal position, and if its form is *concave* the image will expand into an ellipse, with the long axis horizontal when the eyepiece is *inside* the best focus and an ellipse with vertical long axis *outside* the focus. With a *convex* surface the appearances will be reversed. The test is a very searching one, and minute amounts of sphericity can be detected by its use.

Curved Test-plates.

The making of a master test-plate against which other spherical surfaces are to be examined, calls for especial skill and care; but the task is made easier by employing a method suggested by A. E. Conrady several years ago. The underlying idea was first introduced when attempting to check the radii of microscope lenses; concave test-plates were made to fit (by Newton's rings) a previously made hyper-hemisphere of glass, which could be measured by micrometer gauge

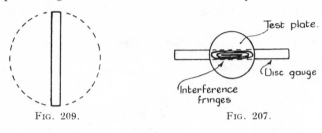

FIG. 209.   FIG. 207.

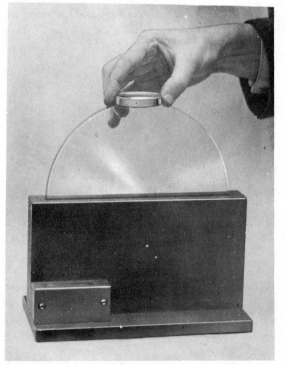

FIG. 208.
Disc Gauge.

across its equatorial diameter.   Such a measurement can be accurately taken and, moreover, any error will be halved as far as the radius is concerned; for example, it is found that radii up to half an inch can be secured to within 0·001 mm. (one thousandth of a millimetre) of their prescribed value by this method.

In order to extend this principle for use with longer radius test-plates, a procedure involving *disc-gauges* was utilized. Obviously a complete hyper-hemisphere of glass of, say, one foot in diameter (for a 6-inch radius) would be both cumbersome and wasteful of glass, so that whilst keeping the diameter, only a narrow (half inch wide) equatorial zone is used (see Fig. 207). The edges of this so-called disc-gauge are polished until the extreme diameter is twice the specified radius. By resting the polished test-plate down on to the disc-gauge (see Fig. 208) elongated Newton's rings will be seen between the surfaces somewhat as indicated in Fig. 209 and only if a complete fit is obtained will the fringes extend over the full diameter of the test plate. The diameter of a disc for use up to six inches can be measured to within 1/100 mm., which represents an accuracy of 1/200 mm., in the radius, or 0·003 per cent.

This is considerably better than that obtainable with the sphero-meter, whose accuracy for a similar radius is of the order 0·03 per cent.

When once the correct radius of the concave test-plate has been attained, a convex test-plate is made to fit the former so that a uniform interference colour is seen over the whole area.

Angle Measurement of Prisms, Parallel Plates, etc.

The testing of prisms for angle is an important part of the optical workshop routine. The general order of accuracy demanded by most work is to within five minutes of arc of the specified angle, but there are a number of cases when the accuracy called for is to within a few seconds of arc.

One of the more convenient methods for such measurements is to use a back-reflecting telescope in conjunction with a horizontal table having a graduated circle. Such a form of goniometer is shown dia-grammatically in Fig. 210. The telescope is fitted with a small side-tube carrying a cross-line, the light from which is reflected down the telescope, rendered parallel by the object-glass, back-reflected from the face of the prism under test, and brought to a focus in the plane of the Ramsden eyepiece, where there is a second cross-line. (The distance AB and BC are arranged to be equal). So that in order to measure the angle DEF, for example, an image of the cross-line A is received from the faces DE and EF in turn, the angle reading on

the divided circle being taken in each case. The prism angle will be
the compliment of that read off the rotating prism table. It will be
realized that both telescope and prism table should be rigidly mounted
on the same base and that the circle should be divided according to

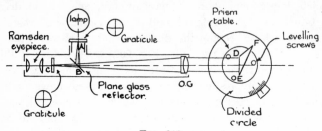

FIG. 210.
Goniometer (Diagrammatic).

the accuracy required, but for most cases if the reading by vernier
is to 30 seconds of arc this will generally suffice.

Right-angled and Sixty Degree Prisms.

The instrument described in the foregoing paragraph will allow
the measurement of a prism with any numerical value for its angle,

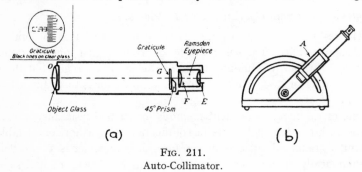

FIG. 211.
Auto-Collimator.

although it necessarily must be well and accurately made. But a
large number of prisms in optical work are right-angled prisms with
two forty-five degree angles, or prisms which utilize a right-angle in
their construction (such as a pentagonal prism, for example), and a
much simpler and less costly instrument can be used for the measurement of such prism angles. This is the auto-collimator, the optical

system of which is shown in Fig. 211a. The graticule G is mounted at the focus of the object glass and the zero line of this graticule is illuminated by light passing through the small 45 degree prism as indicated, so that if the parallel beam thus emerging from the objective is received on to a truly plane mirror, it can be reflected back into the object-glass and brought to a focus again in the plane of the scale. If the scale is divided in tenths of a millimetre and the focal length of the O.G. is 33·3 cm. (approx. thirteen inches), each division will correspond to an angular subtense of 1 minute of arc; and using a fairly high power Ramsden eyepiece a fifth of one scale division can be estimated, corresponding to twelve seconds of arc. The auto-

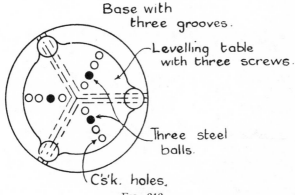

FIG. 212.
Levelling Table for use with Auto-Collimator.

collimator tube can be held in a suitable metal stand shown in Fig. 211b, the arm A being swung into any desired position within the semi-circle and clamped by a winged nut. A levelling table having three balls on its upper surface (see Fig. 212) for resting the prisms or plates on, will complete the apparatus.

Tests with the Auto-Collimator.

In order to determine the error in the 90° angle the auto-collimator may be directed towards the hypotenuse face of the prism, when two brightly illuminated images of the graticule zero line will be seen in the eyepiece. These images come from light which has been internally reflected from the other two faces and has again emerged from the hypotenuse. If α is the error from the true 90° angle, then ray (1) Fig. 213 will undergo a change in direction of 2α.N., when N is the refractive index of the glass; similarly, ray (2) will be deviated by this amount, and consequently the total angular separation of the images as measured on the eyepiece scale will be N.4α. Assuming a nominal refractive index of 1·5, the error measured with the auto-collimator will therefore be six times the real error of the ninety degree angle.

This measurement, whilst giving the numerical value of the error, does not tell us whether the angle is greater or less than ninety. To determine this, it is advisable to place the prism very carefully in

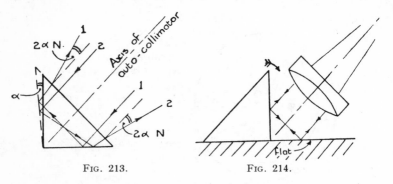

FIG. 213.   FIG. 214.

contact with an optically flat surface (see Fig. 214), direct the auto-collimator as indicated, and measure the error in the exterior angle—this will be a check on the previous method—then whilst observing, the prism should be tilted over in the direction of the arrow and the direction in which the two images move should be noted. If the two images *come together* the exterior angle must be *greater* than ninety degrees, whereas if they *continue to separate* the exterior angle must be *less* than ninety. With this knowledge and the magnitude of the error, the real value of the so-called ninety angle may be obtained.

To determine the absolute values of the 45° angles the prism should be rested on the three steel balls mounting indicated in Fig. 215 and a reflection received from the hypotenuse face only.—To prevent confusion from the other reflected images, the prism face AC and BC should be smeared with vaseline.—Having noted the reading of the reflected image on the eyepiece scale, the prism is now removed and placed on the three steel balls, such that the face AC now occupies that previously occupied by BC; the reading on the scale is again noted. The angular amount thus read off will represent twice the difference in angle between A and B. By observing the direction in which the image has moved, it can be shown which is the larger of the two angles; and in this way (with a knowledge of the value of the 90° angle) the true values of the 45° angles can be determined.

Sixty Degree Angles.

The prism is rested on the three steel balls and the auto-collimator arranged to receive light reflected from the face AB (Fig. 216)   The

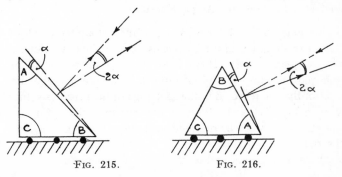

FIG. 215.   FIG. 216.

reflected image line is read on the eyepiece scale; the prism is then turned round so that the angle C occupies the position previously held by A and the reading again taken on the scale.   This difference in angle as given on the scale will be equal to twice the difference between angle A and angle C.   Similarly, by placing angle B in the position of angle A, the difference of B from A may be obtained.   Hence B and C can be expressed in terms of A in the equation $A + B + C = 180°$ Having therefore determined the absolute value of angle A, those for B and C may also be obtained.

Parallel Plates.

Lack of parallelism of the two faces of a so-called parallel plate can be determined by receiving reflected images from the upper and lower surfaces of the plate (see Fig. 217) and measuring the angular separation θ indicated on the eyepiece scale of the auto-collimator.

The angle α (which is the error in parallelism) can be shown to be equal to $1/2\ (\theta/N)$ and if the refractive index N is taken as 1·5, $\theta/3$ will give the real angle α.

It is useful also to know the direction of the " prism " on such a plate, and by rotating the latter in its own plane on the steel balls the two images will vary in separation. The position at which maximum separation occurs will give the " prism " direction.

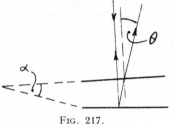

FIG. 217.

Naked Eye Methods for Angle Measurement.

Right-angled prisms having 45 degree angles may be tested for angle to within two minutes of arc by means of the naked eye alone without any special apparatus. If we hold a right-angled prism at arms length and look into the hypotenuse face, we see a virtual image of the iris of the eye reflected in the roof edge of the prism (see Fig. 218). Assuming rays (1) and (2) going towards the prism from the edges of the iris AB, they will return from reflection along the same paths if the right-angle is truly ninety degrees, and a circular image of the iris will be seen as indicated on the left of the diagram.

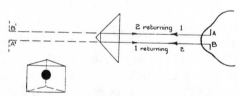

FIG. 218.
Naked Eye Tests on Prisms (90° Angle Correct).

If the right angle is *less* than 90 degrees, the rays (1) and (2) returning after reflection (see Fig. 219) will give virtual images A¹ and B′ of the iris AB and the appearance will be that of an elliptical image with its long axis at right angles to the roof edge. Whereas, if the right angle is *greater* than ninety degrees (see Fig. 220), the appearance will be that of a contracted image of the iris with the short axis of the ellipse at right angles to the roof edge (i.e., a cat's eye appearance).

In order to obtain an idea of the numerical accuracy available by this simple but effective method, let us assume that the error in the ninety degree angle is α; then from Fig. 213 the total deviation between

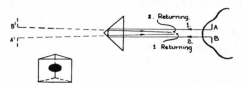

FIG. 219.
Right Angle less than 90°.

the two rays (1) and (2) emerging from the prism will be N.4α, and with N = 1·50 the magnification effect will be six times that of the actual angle α.   So that if the error in the ninety angle was one minute

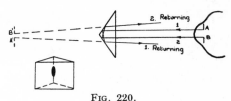

FIG. 220.
Right Angle greater than 90°.

of arc, this would be seen as six minutes.   Now, as the prism is held at arm's length (say, 24 inches) six minutes of arc corresponds to $0·0017 \times 24 = 0·041$ inch or 1 millimetre.   The average diameter of the

FIG. 221.
Test on Base Angles.

pupil iris may be taken as 4 mm., so that 1 mm. variation is round-ness of the image should   be easily detectable; thus it will be seen that the test is a fairly critical one and it is rather surprising to find that an accuracy of one or two minutes of arc can be obtained numerically without any auxiliary apparatus whatever.   Errors in the ninety angle exceeding ten minutes of arc may result in images of two complete eyes being seen, and the separation of these can be measured by holding a millimetre scale on white celluloid close to the lower lid of the eye so that the reflected image of this is seen in juxtaposition with the image of the two pupils.

Test on the 45° Base Angles.

The difference in error between the two base angles of such a prism may be tested by viewing a distant object after reflection externally and internally from the hypotenuse face shown in Fig. 221b.

A boldly marked cross-line (Fig. 221a) with divisions marked on it corresponding to 5 minute intervals is set up at, say, ten yards distance; the observer then places his eye quite close to the prism

FIG. 222.
Naked Eye Test for Flatness of a Surface.

edge and obtains a reflection obliquely from the hypotenuse face. By moving the eye slowly below this edge the internally reflected image will be seen, and by suitable adjustment both images can be seen simultaneously. Unless the base angles are exactly equal (which is rather rare) their difference may be read off the angular scale by noting the vertical displacement of the horizontal line. Assuming the refractive index of the glass is 1·5 and if nearly grazing of the light is used, it can be shown that the observed angular separation between the two reflected images is equal to the difference betwen the two base angles. An accuracy of about 2 to 3 minutes of arc is obtainable by this method. If a lateral displacement of the vertical line is observed pyramidal error in the prism will be indicated.

Naked Eye Test for Flatness of a Surface.

The test of a flat surface by oblique reflection is so sensitive that even the naked eye will detect quite a low degree of sphericity if nearly grazing incidence is employed. If a dotted cross, Fig. 222, is set up at a distance and an image of this is viewed in the surface so as to send light from the full length of the plate through the pupil of the eye, then any astigmatism resulting from the spherical form of the surface will cause the dots of either the vertical or horizontal line to merge together into a grey line. It may be estimated that the naked eye will thus detect a radius of curvature up to about ten thousand times the length of the surface being tested, provided that the surface measures at least several times the diameter of the pupil.

Pyramidal Error.

In Fig. 223a, let the plane ABC be perpendicular to OA, and let AP be drawn perpendicular to BC, meeting it in P. If we join OP, then the angle AOP is a measure of the pyramidal error.

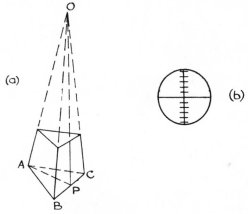

Fig. 223.
Pyramidal Error of Prisms.

In order to measure this possible error, it is desirable to use a goniometer, such as that shown in Fig. 210, but with a graticule in the eyepiece of the form given in Fig. 223b. The telescope is directed towards faces AB and AC in turn, and the levelling screws of the prism table, together with the tilt of the telescope in a vertical plane, are adjusted so that the back reflected image of the horizontal graticule line falls on the real horizontal line in each case. When this adjustment has been effected, the edge AO of the prism must be perpendicular to the optical axis of the telescope.

If, now, the telescope is directed towards the face BC the displacement of the back-reflected horizontal line image can be measured on the vertical angular scale; this displacement will be equal to twice the angle AOP.

Non-reflecting Films on Glass.

When light passes through any optical system a small fraction of the incident light is reflected at each air-glass surface, and if the

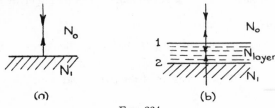

(a)　　　　　　　　(b)

FIG. 224.

number of surfaces is large (for example, with a terrestrial telescope having ten air-glass surfaces), the loss of light by reflection may amount to one-third of the total incident light; this is irrespective of light lost by absorption in the glass. The amount of light lost by reflection at normal incidence on a well-polished glass surface is given by Fresnel as

$$\left(\frac{N_1 - N_0}{N_1 + N_0}\right)^2$$

where N_0 is the refractive index of the first medium and N_1 the second medium (Fig. 224a), so that from 4 to 7 per cent. is likely to occur at any one air-glass surface depending on whether the glass is a crown or a dense flint. This relation is very closely correct also for angles of incidence up to twenty degrees.

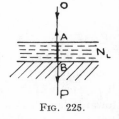

FIG. 225.

If now a thin layer or film of material of correct refractive index is placed on the glass surface, the reflected light can be considerably reduced. It can be shown that the correct refractive index to employ for such a film is given by the square root of the product of N_0 and N_1, that is $N_{LAYER} = \sqrt{N_0 \times N_1}$.

So that if we were dealing with a glass of $N_1 = 1.65$, for example, the required refractive index of the layer or film would be 1.28. Applying the Fresnel relation to surfaces 1 and 2 (Fig. 224b) in turn we have:—

At first surface
$$\left(\frac{N_L - N_o}{N_L + N_o}\right)^2 = \left(\frac{1 \cdot 28 - 1}{2 \cdot 28}\right)^2 = 0 \cdot 015 \text{ or } 1 \cdot 5 \text{ per cent. lost by reflection.}$$

At second surface
$$\left(\frac{N_1 - N_L}{N_1 + N_L}\right)^2 = \left(\frac{1 \cdot 65 - 1 \cdot 28}{2 \cdot 93}\right)^2 = 0 \cdot 16 \text{ or } 1 \cdot 6 \text{ per cent. lost by reflection.}$$

Therefore total loss by reflection = **3·1 per cent.**

Whereas, if no film was present, the loss = $\left(\frac{1 \cdot 65 - 1}{2 \cdot 65}\right)^2 = 0 \cdot 060$ or **6 per cent.**

It is clear, therefore, that by interposing a layer of material of suitable refractive index, the loss by reflection may be reduced by half.

The second and more important part of such a procedure is to arrange that the non-reflecting film is of a suitable thinness, for by so doing the reflected light can be eliminated by interference and the transmitted light increased.

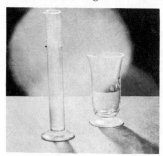 

Illustrating the advantage to be gained by Coating the Lens Surfaces of a Photographic Lens with a Non-Reflecting Film. *[Photographs by H. A. Dell.]*

Referring to Fig. 225, a portion of the incident light will be reflected at A and after entering the film-layer a further portion will be reflected at B. The path difference in these two beams travelling in the direction AO will be $2AB \times N_L$ and for interference to occur this quantity should be equal to $\lambda/2$.

[N.B.—There is a phase-change of $\lambda/2$ at both A and B, for in each case the reflection is at a rarer-to-denser medium.]

Thus, in order that no light should be lost in the direction AO, the thickness of the layer AB should be $\lambda/(2 \times 2 \times N_L) = \lambda/5$ for $N_L = 1 \cdot 28$.

For light which is proceeding on in the direction BP the retardation of the portion of the beam which is reflected at B and again at A and then sent on in the direction BP, will be $2AB \times N_L = 2N_L.\lambda/5$, and as there is a phase change of $\lambda/2$ at the point B only (not at A in this case), the light will be re-inforced.

Consequently, no light will be lost by reflection and the transmitted light will be increased.

In practice there is no material with $N_L = 1\cdot28$ which can be put on a glass surface, so that the nearest approach to this has to be employed. At the present time Cryolite (Aluminium fluoride) $N_D = 1\cdot36$ and Magnesium fluoride are used. The films are deposited by the high vacuum volatilization process[*]; the powdered fluoride is evaporated by heating it electrically in a vacuum (10^{-4} mm. Hg.) and it then condenses in a vitreous film on any relatively cool surface directly exposed to the source. Estimation of the thickness of a non-reflecting film is carried out (whilst the glass surface being coated is still in the vacuum) by reflecting white light from it and by observation of the interference colours so produced. As the wavelength of zero reflection moves through the visible spectrum, the reflected light becomes orange, purple, blue and green, or in successive orders of interference colours. For optical instruments intended for visual work, the colour of the film should be purple, denoting maximum transmission in the yellow-green, whilst for optical components intended for photographic work an orange colour is generally desired.

Non-reflecting films can also be produced by chemical means and by artificial weathering processes, particulars of which may be found in the references [1], [2], [3] below.

Fig. 226a and b are photographs taken with a lens-system before and after being treated with a non-reflecting film. It will be noticed how the stray and scattered light has been reduced by utilizing this process.

Interferometer Tests.

A method of testing optical parts by interferometric means was developed by Twyman[4] some years ago. The type of interferometer

---

[*] British Patent No. 538,272.
[1] K. B. Blodgett—*Phys. Rev.*, Vol. 55, p. 391 (1939).
[2] H. D. Taylor—*The Adjustment and Testing of Telescope Objectives.*
[3] F. H. Nicoll—*R.C.A. Review*, Vol. 6, p. 287 (1942).
[4] F. Twyman. *Phil. Mag.*, Jan. 1918, p. 49.
  ,,   *Photographic Journal*, Nov. 1918, p. 239.
  ,,   *Astrophys. Journ.*, 1918, Vol. 48, p. 256.

used for this purpose is a modification of the Michelson form (described in most text books) and its principle will be understood by referring to Fig. 227.

Monochromatic light is focused on to a small hole H situated at the focus of the lens L_1. The parallel beam leaving this lens strikes a half-silvered mirror M_1 inclined at 45 degrees to the axis, part of it being reflected in a direction M_3 and part transmitted towards M_2. The two beams are then reflected back by the two wholly silvered mirrors M_2 and M_3, pass through the lens L_2 and are brought to a focus at E where the eye is placed. By adjustment of the distances M_1M_2 and M_1M_3, the optical lengths of the two paths may be made equal, and by further fine-adjustment for tilt of the mirrors the two images of H formed at E may be made to coincide exactly. When

this is the case, a uniform field of illumination will be seen by the eye at E, and the system can be looked upon as though it provides two perfectly plane wave-fronts coinciding in a plane such as that indicated by the dotted line F. If now one of these wave-fronts (say, from mirror M_2) is distorted in some way by the introduction of something which retards the beam from M_2, then the field will no longer appear uniform to the eye at E but dark interference fringes will be seen wherever the retardation of the beam from M_2

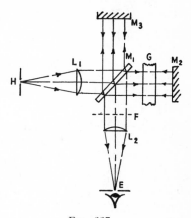

FIG. 227.

is half a wavelength or an odd number of half-wavelengths behind the corresponding part of the beam from M_3.

For example, let us imagine that an optically plane parallel plate of glass (which is *not* homogeneous throughout) is placed at G, then the appearance seen might be similar to that indicated in Fig. 228 (a). Such interference fringes would be due to a retardation caused by the variation of velocity of the light in its passage through the block of glass, or in other words due to a change of refractive index throughout the glass. It is important to notice that the shape of any particular fringe indicates the region where the refractive index is the same, and thus the appearance seen may be looked upon as a contour map of the glass block in terms of variation of path length of the light in passing through the block. Hence, any particular fringe indicates a path length of N.t, where N is the refractive index of the material and t its thickness; it must be remembered, however, that when the specimen is placed in the interferometer the light travels through the block *twice* and therefore the total retardation corresponding to any particular fringe is equal to 2.N.t.

This at once brings out the usefulness of the interferometer as a workshop tool, for having seen the contour map thus presented, and having marked on the surface of the glass the "high" regions, one can proceed to polish these down by local hand polishing (sometimes called "figuring") until the field appears uniform and free from fringes. In practice it is of course essential to know which are "high"

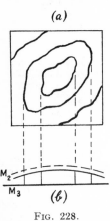

(a)

M_2

M_3　　(b)

Fig. 228.

regions and which are "low" regions; this may be carried out by observing the movement of the fringes when either one of the optical path lengths M_1M_2 or M_1M_3 is increased. If for example we imagine Fig. 228 (b) to be a sectional view of the wave-fronts at position F (Fig. 227) and then increase the path-length M_1M_2 by a slight pressure with the finger on the metal base of the instrument near M_2, then the wave-front M_2 (Fig. 228b) will be "pulled away" from the plane wave-front M_3, and for any particular fringe to maintain its previous path-difference it must (in the case shown in the diagram) move *outwards*; that is, the fringes would appear to expand from a centre. If such an appear-

ance was observed, it would indicate that the shape of the wave-front M_2 (Fig. 228 b) was concave facing the plane wave-front M_3 and therefore that the light passing through the centre of the glass block had been retarded with respect to that passing through the outer positions. In order to reduce this retardation in the central region, obviously it will be necessary to reduce the thickness of the glass in this region (by local polishing) and therefore the central interference fringe when marked on the surface would be indicated as "high."

It should be pointed out that the interference fringes seen may be due, either to lack of homogeneity of the glass or due to lack of planeness of the surface, or to both; but as the interferometer records the combined effect (namely $2 \cdot N \cdot t$ as already explained) it is only necessary to figure one surface until the quantity $2 \cdot N \cdot t$ is similar for the whole area of the specimen under test.

Apart from using the interferometer as a means of testing the homogeneity of transparent materials or the planeness of surfaces it may also be used for testing the regularity of optical path when light passes through a prism, a lens system or even a complete optical instrument.

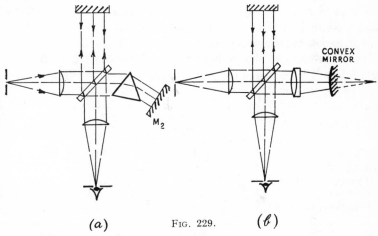

(a) FIG. 229. (b)

Fig. 229 (a) and (b) show the modifications necessary when testing a 60° prism and a lens respectively. In the former case the plane mirror M_2 is rotated so that the light is returned through the prism when the latter is in its minimum deviation position. In the latter case, a truly spherical convex mirror is mounted in the convergent beam produced by the lens, and is adjusted (by means of an accurate micrometer screw) so that its centre of curvature coincides with the focus of the lens. The characteristic interference patterns corresponding to the various aberrations of a lens system and the interpretations thereof have been studied by R. Kingslake* and are contained in a paper which will prove helpful to the advanced worker. A further reference is also given below.

* R. Kingslake. *Trans. Opt. Soc.*, 1925, Vol. 27, pp. 94-105.
  Dict. Applied Physics, Vol. 4, p. 147.

APPENDIX

The Cleaning of Optical Surfaces.

A high state of surface cleanliness is of considerable importance in optical work. When lenses and prisms are to be mounted in their instruments (especially when the latter are sealed and made airtight) it is of primary importance that the glass surfaces should be perfectly clean. Not only does this reduce loss of light, but a surface free from contamination remains clean for a longer period.

It has already been shown that some 4 to 7 per cent. of the incident light is lost by reflection at an air-glass surface, and the following table may be of interest: —

Type of Telescope.	Number of Reflecting Surfaces.	Loss by Reflection.
Galilean.	4	15 per cent.
Astronomical.	6	22 ,,
Terrestrial (with lens erector).	10	33 ,,
Prismatic (two prism).	10	33 ,,

If therefore, the glass surfaces were not thoroughly clean, an additional 5 per cent. or more might be lost at each surface, with the result that double the amount given in the above table would be lost, representing a transmission of only about one-third of the incident light in the case of a prismatic binocular, for example. This emphasizes the importance of having really clean surfaces in optical instruments.

The first steps in cleaning optical work is to free the surfaces from any trace of grease. This is best done by immersing the glass in a caustic potash solution or by well swabbing the surface with benzene. It should then be washed thoroughly with soap and water (the natural oil from the fingers must not come near the surface and it is advisable, therefore, to wear rubber gloves). Rinsing in distilled water should then be carried out and the surface wiped with a clean (well-washed) linen cloth. A light swabbing with a 50 per cent. nitric acid solution should now be given and the surface again rinsed. Finally wipe the surface with alcohol and dry it off with another piece of well-laundered linen.

It has been suggested that the last operation in the cleaning process should be to rub the surface firmly with a piece of freshly cut elder pith.

Test for a Clean Surface—Breath Figure.

If there is any contamination of a glass surface left by the cleaning process it may be tested by breathing gently on the surface, for in this case the breath will condense in tiny droplets of water which will be seen as a film on the surface. But should the surface be *really* clean, the water vapour will condense in such minute and uniform drops that the film will be quite invisible, and gives the impression that the breath will not "take" to the surface.

Rayleigh[1] and Baker[2] have stated that if the tip of a blowpipe flame is passed quickly over a so-called clean surface, the latter will then be so clean that it will not "take" a breath figure.

When optical parts are mounted in instruments which are sealed up in order to ward off the effects of weather, etc., the surfaces sometimes become "cloudy" or "filmed" even though they may have been thoroughly cleaned previously. (This is best detected by looking at a source of light through the instrument in the reverse direction to which it is used.)

Some of the causes of this "filming" of surfaces are as follows:—

(1) Condensation caused by change of temperature and humidity.

(2) Lubricant in the instrument giving off volatile constituents which condense on the surfaces.

(3) Instruments with aluminium bodies giving off water vapour held in the pores of the metal.

(4) Imperfect cleaning of the glass surfaces (i.e. some contamination which causes nuclei for the condensation of moisture).

(5) Instability of the glass itself.

Whilst some of these troubles may be cured by paying attention to the acid content of the lubricants employed, and also to complete drying-out of the body-tubes of the instruments, it has been shown

[1] Rayleigh—*Scientific Papers*—Vol. 6—p. 26 and p. 27 (Cambridge University Press—1920).
[2] T. J. Baker—*Phil. Mag.*—44—752 (1922).

that most of the difficulties connected with the deposition of minute globular particles on the glass surfaces can be overcome or greatly lessened by exercising great care in the thorough cleaning of the optical surfaces before they are mounted in the instruments.

In certain cases, the "filming" has been prevented by immersing the glass in a solution containing 50 per cent. alcohol, 45 per cent. distilled water, and 5 per cent. nitric acid for about half an hour prior to cleaning.

Balsaming.

Many optical components (such as achromatic lenses, compound prisms, etc.) are cemented together with Canada balsam. This is a resinous material containing turpentine; the latter can be evaporated off by heating so as to obtain balsam of varying degrees of hardness, sometimes distinguished as hard, medium and soft.

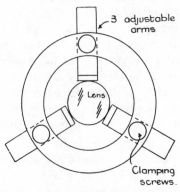

FIG. 230.
Balsaming Jig.

The relative hardness may be tested by means of the viscometer (described on page 207). In practice, soft and medium are more generally used, and can be obtained already filtered and clear in quality.

The process of balsaming consists in having a thick iron plate on three legs heated from below by a ring burner; the plate is covered with a piece of white paper and the lens components (already cleaned) are laid on it and covered with a suitable lid to prevent draughts coming near the glass work whilst heating up. The pot of balsam should also be on the hot plate. When the optical parts are well warmed, a small quantity of the liquid balsam is taken from the pot with a metal rod and placed in the centre of the concave lens component; the other lens is then put down on top of the balsam and the

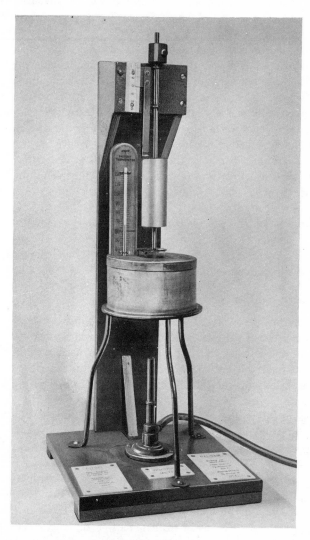

Fig. 231.
Viscometer for Pitch and Balsam.

latter is spread out into a thin layer by exerting pressure on the top lens with a cork, giving it a slight rotary movement at the same time. Any air bubbles which have become trapped in the balsam film can thus be removed. The lenses are held together by pressure over their centres and allowed to cool, when the surplus balsam at the edges may be wiped off with a cloth dipped in xylol.

The baking process must then be carried out in order to harden the balsam and thus prevent the components from moving about when subjected to a rise in temperature under natural conditions (e.g. in hot climates). The cemented work is, therefore, placed in a suitable oven (electrically or gas heated) fitted with a thermometer, and baked continuously for a certain period of time. For the soft balsam this time should be about fifty hours at 70°C., whilst for the medium hardness balsam a period of three hours at 40°C. will suffice. On no account should the glass work be taken out of the oven until the latter has cooled down slowly (about 20° per hour), otherwise insufficient annealing will result.

During the baking process it may be necessary to mount the optical work in a suitable jig or clamp to prevent the parts sliding over one another. For instance, a three-jaw chuck of the type shown in Fig. 230 can prove useful for lens work.

Viscometer for Pitch and Balsam.

The hardness of pitch laps employed in polishing processes is of importance; for if the pitch is too soft the lap will soon go out of shape owing to the flow of the pitch, whilst if too hard the glass surface being polished will become scratched, due to the fact that any small particles falling on the pitch will not sink in before the damage has been done.

In earlier days the hardness was frequently judged by the glass-worker pressing his thumb-nail into the pitch. If an indentation could just be made, this was considered as the correct hardness; obviously such a method was only a rough guide and it is now considered desirable to have a better control on the judgment of the hardness. To this end a piece of apparatus shown in Fig. 231 may be used; it consists of a piece of quarter-inch steel rod, conical at the end (about 14° angle) terminating in a small flat half a millimetre in diameter. Attached to this is a cylinder of lead, the whole weighing 1,000 grammes. The point of the rod is allowed to bear on the surface of the pitch (or other substance whose viscosity it is desired to measure) contained in a small vessel which is immersed in water and kept at any desired temperature. The length of time taken for the rod to fall a given distance is determined. The temperature may be standardised at 70°F., in which case the rod and weight should sink 2 mm. in four minutes for a correct average hardness of pitch for general purposes.

The apparatus can also be used for controlling the viscosity of balsam, and in this case (for medium hardness) the rod and weight should sink 25 mm. in three and a half minutes at 70°F.

Silvering.

The two chemical silvering processes most generally used in optical work are Brashear's method and the Rochelle salt method. The former is used to obtain thick coatings on surface-silvered mirrors which may have to be burnished at intervals; whilst the second method, owing to its slower action, is suitable for making partially silvered mirrors such as interferometer plates.

Success is rarely obtained unless scrupulous care is taken in cleaning the surfaces to be silvered and also the vessels in which the process is to be carried out.

Brashear* Method.

Four solutions are made up to the following formulæ: —

Reducing Solution 1.*A*	OR	*Reducing Solution* 1.*B*
(must be aged for two or four weeks)		(can be used without ageing)
		120 cc. distilled water
500 cc. distilled water		8 gm. dextrose sugar
45 gm. sugar		
2 cc. nitric acid (concentrated)		
88 cc. alcohol		

Solution 2.	*Solution* 3.	*Solution* 4.
300 cc. distilled water	100 cc. distilled water	30 cc. distilled water
20 gm. silver nitrate	14 gm. potassium hydroxide	2 gm. silver nitrate

Procedure: —Add ammonia (concentrated) to solution 2 until a dark brown precipitate of silver oxide forms and begins to clear. Then put in solution 4 *drop by drop* until a distinct straw colour is seen (this is to avoid excess ammonia). Now add slowly all of solution 3 and stir all the time.

* J. A. Brashear—*English Mechanic*—Vol. 31—p. 237 (1880)

Again add ammonia until the solution just clears, and again drop by drop of solution 4 until it takes on a straw colour.

The foregoing solution may now be filtered. The last operation is to mix in 120 cc. of the reducing solution 1.A or B, and then to pour the whole over the mirror to be silvered.

The silver will come down fairly rapidly (about ten minutes) and deposit a tenacious and hard layer. The mirror can then be taken out of the solution and rubbed dry with a cotton-wool pad. It may then be polished with a chamois leather charged with rouge.

Rochelle Salt Method.

Two solutions are required for this method. Solution 1 is made as follows:—5 gm. of silver nitrate are dissolved in 300 cc. of distilled water and ammoniated (as already described in the Brashear method) so that the silver oxide precipitate formed is almost but not completely clear, and presents the straw colour appearance. This is filtered and diluted with water to 500 cc.

In solution 2, 1 gm. of silver nitrate is dissolved in 500 cc. of water; it is then brought to a boil, and 0.83 gm. of Rochelle salt (dissolved in a little water) is added.

To silver a mirror, equal volumes of the two solutions are mixed together and poured at once into the silvering dish.

As the silver is deposited much more slowly by this process, an hour may be required for a thick deposit to form; so that partial reflecting films are obtained by withdrawing the mirror from the solution at the appropriate time. In order not to disturb the mirror, however, auxiliary small glass plates may be inserted in the dish and removed periodically so that the progress of the deposition may be judged.

On removal from the dish, the mirror is rinsed in distilled water and allowed to dry, after which it can be polished with a powder puff and optical rouge.

Photographic Items.

One of the most useful applications of photographic processes in optics or in physics generally is the copying of diagrams, illustrations, pages of print, etc., for the purpose of making lantern slides; but the method is so well known that no mention need be made of it here. What is of greater interest, however, is the fact that modern photographic emulsions have a much smaller *average grain size* than they did only a few years ago, and this means that much greater reductions of the object (to be copied) can be made without the image suffering from "graininess." In other words, as the resolving power of the plate has been increased, we can produce much smaller image intervals photographically than has hitherto been the case. A few examples are: the advent of microfilm methods* for copying documents on to standard 35 mm. film; the increase in the use of microphotographs as distinct from photomicrographs; and the making of diffraction gratings and graticules.

The average grain size of fine-grained process plates has for some years now been about 0.005 mm., but the modern " high resolution " plates or films are between ten to fifty times smaller in average grain size, i.e. approximately 0.0002 mm. This means that (allowing for the usual safety factor multiple of ten on the grain size) something of the order of 500 lines per mm. or 13,000 lines per inch can now be photographed provided always that the lens used for copying gives good definition and that it is working at sufficient aperture to give an equal resolving power.

Graticules.

The making of small eyepiece scales for optical instruments frequently requires to be done; for although there is a fair variety of graticule types which can be purchased, there never seems to be just the one which is desired for a particular purpose in the laboratory. The design for the graticule is first drawn out in Indian ink on white card; it is then set up on the usual copying bench and the camera arranged at a suitable distance to give the desired reduction (a very usual diameter of the finished graticule is about three quarters of an inch). The image is focused carefully—it may be necessary to employ a low-power microscope for doing this—and the photograph taken, using one of the so-called " high resolution " plates now available. A special developer is given for use with these plates or films, and it is essential to use this to obtain the best results. The negative thus obtained should preferably be put in an intensifier solution, and when dry, contact positives are made using the same type of " high resolution " plate.

* B. K. Johnson—*Proc. Brit. Soc. International Bibliography*—1942—Vol. 4. p. 25.

Excellent results are obtainable by this method, the edges of the lines showing no trace whatever of "graininess" when viewed under the highest power eyepieces used in optical instruments.

Developers.

Hydroquinone (for plates) when contrast is required.

Solution A.

Hydroquinone	25 gm.
Potassium Metabisulphite	25 gm.
Potassium Bromide	12 gm.
Water (to make)	1,000 cc.

Solution B.

Potassium Hydrate	50 gm.
Water	1,000 cc.

Solutions A and B should be kept in separate bottles, and mixed in equal quantities when required for use.

M.Q. (for plates and gaslight papers) general use.

Metol	4 gm.
Hydroquinone	15 gm.
Sodium Sulphite (cryst.)	105 gm.
Sodium Carbonate (anhydrous)	100 gm.
Potassium Bromide	1 gm.
Water (to make)	1,000 cc.

Fine-grain developer (high resolution plates).

Elon	1.25 gm.
Sodium Sulphite (cryst.)	45 gm.
Hydroquinone	6 gm.
Sodium Carbonate (cryst.)	80 gm.
Potassium Bromide	0.5 gm.
Water (to make)	1,000 cc.

Fixing Bath.

Hyposulphite	150 gm.
Potassium Metabisulphite	25 gm.
Water (to make)	1,000 cc.

The time of development may be controlled by noting the time taken for the image first to appear and multiplying this by a time-factor of six, the latter figure giving the total time for complete development. Alternatively, one may standardize the development by keeping the developer at 65°F. (measured by thermometer) and always giving four minutes.

Processing Dufay Colour Film.

There are certain cases in scientific work where colour photographs are an advantage over the monochrome; for example, when illustrating polarization effects, fluorescent effects, etc., and the method for development of the coloured transparency by one of these processes, namely the Dufay Chromex system, is given below.

As the process has to be carried out in total darkness for part of the time, it is advisable to use a dark-room clock with a piece of self-luminous radium compound attached to the second and minute hands; this has proved less nerve-racking than using an alarm. This remark applies also when developing panchromatic plates.

Procedure:—

Immerse film or plate in the developer (solution 1) for five and a half minutes—rock dish violently.

After development, rinse and place negative in the *stop-bath* for two minutes.

Transfer to *bleaching solution* for five minutes.

Light may be turned on after one minute in bleaching bath and all subsequent operations carried out in white light.

After rinsing, place negative in *clearing-bath* until the brown stain has disappeared (usually a few seconds).

Now expose the film or plate for four minutes held at three feet from a 100-watt lamp.

Then give a second development in solution 1 for four to five minutes.

Developer (solution 1).

Metol	1 gm.
Sodium Sulphite (cryst.)	100 gm.
Hydroquinone	8 gm.
Sodium Carbonate (cryst.)	100 gm.
Potassium Thiocyanate	9 gm.
Potassium Bromide	5 gm.
Water (to make)	1,000 cc.

Stop bath.

Solution of Acetic Acid	1 per cent.

H

Bleaching bath.

Potassium Permanganate	..	..	2 gm.
Sulphuric Acid (conc.) ..	..	..	10 cc.
Water (to make) ..	..	..	.. 1,000 cc.

Clearing bath.

Potassium Metabisulphite	..	..	25 gm.
Water (to make) ..	..	..	.. 1,000 cc.

Reflex Printing.

Frequently a copy on paper of a certain page or diagram in a book is required for one's notes. Instead of taking a photograph on a plate and then making an enlargement from this, satisfactory prints may be taken by resting a piece of gaslight printing paper on the upper glass surface of the ordinary printing frame illuminated by lamps from below, and then placing the copy in contact with the emulsion side of the printing paper. On exposure the light travels through the printing paper and is back-reflected to the emulsion by the white portions of the copy, no light being received from the black parts.

On development in the usual way, the print will consist of a negative with white letters on a black background, and with the reading matter from right to left. This paper negative must now be laid down on the printing frame and a further piece of paper placed in contact and a positive print taken in the ordinary way.

The foregoing method is necessary if the page to be copied is printed on *both* sides. If, however, the copy is clear at the back, it is only necessary to place the copy face downwards on the printing frame, put the emulsion side of the gaslight paper in contact with the clear side of the copy and take a print. In this case the letters will also come out white against a black background (this does not matter greatly) but the reading matter will read the correct way round.

Cross-lines.

Many instruments require cross-lines in the focal plane of their eyepieces, and whilst in the past spider-web was generally employed for this purpose, nowadays something more robust is called for so that repair is not required so frequently. Cross-lines on glass are, therefore, much used now and may be produced by diamond ruling, etching, or by photographic methods as already described. One method, however, which does not appear so widely known is to rule two lines at right angle on an unexposed fine-grained photographic plate (e.g. a process plate) in the dark-room in red light, using a razor blade or specially prepared ruling tool. The plate is then developed in the usual way, when it will be found that the ruled lines come up black and very fine against a clear background. They will stand an eyepiece magnification up to twenty times without any appearance of raggedness of the line edge; the crossing-point of the lines is also quite sharply defined and not rounded as sometimes occurs with photographic reduction by a lens.

Should it be desirable to utilize webs for the cross-line, it is necessary first to get the web from a spider (preferably the large brown garden spider found in the autumn) on to a wire frame ($3'' \times 2''$). By allowing the spider to spin his web downwards from the frame, the latter can be rotated so that the web is stretched diagonally across the long edges of the frame (see Fig. 232) and the web held by a drop of quick-drying cement. The metal diaphragm is removed from the eyepiece and the frame laid carefully on to it so that one of the webs rests in a marked position on the diaphragm; two drops of cement (e.g., shellac) are placed at the two ends of the web and allowed to dry; they are then cut off and the process repeated for a position at right angles to the first web. Both spun gold and quartz fibres also make fine threads for cross-lines.

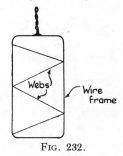

Fig. 232.

Collodion Films.

Very thin (a few wavelengths of light or less) films of materials are useful on many occasions in optical work; for example, they may be used as reflecting plates as in a vertical illuminator or as a protective layer for water soluble crystals such as rocksalt, etc. One of the advantages of these films is that they may be made so thin that no double reflection is noticeable from the two surfaces, and moreover they can be made so uniform both in thickness and planeness that interferometer tests show that they are almost perfect from a path-difference point of view.

One method of making them is to mix by volume one part of collodion (methylated) with two parts of æther; then to pour this solution rapidly over a flat glass plate held in an inclined position and allow it to dry. The film can then be floated off on to water by holding one end of the glass plate slightly below the water level, when the film will gradually begin to lift and come away from the glass. When this has been carried out satisfactorily a metal framework (on which the film is to be mounted) is coated with shellac and gently placed down on to the film; the latter will adhere to the shellaced surface and after mopping up the edges of any superfluous film with a small camel hair brush, the whole may then be carefully lifted off the water. When dry, the collodion film will tighten up and should show a uniform interference colour by reflection if the operation has been well carried out. By varying the ratio of the volumes of the two liquids the thickness of the film can be adjusted.

Waxes and Cements.

Red wax.—The optical-physicist uses waxes and cements for various purposes, such as holding lenses, prisms, mirrors, etc., in their mounts, securing windows into instruments and so forth. The most generally used soft wax is made from beeswax and turpentine mixed in the ratio of about 5 to 1; this is sometimes coloured red, from which this wax often takes its name. The usefulness of this wax lies in its adhesive and plastic properties, for whilst it can be manipulated in the fingers quite readily, it will set fairly rigidly when the warmth from the hand is removed.

Other suitable soft adhesive materials are plasticine and Apiezon compound, although the latter is more suitable for vacuum work.

Beeswax and Resin.

This cement is made by melting together equal parts of beeswax and resin, and forming it into thin sticks when cold. It is particularly suitable for cementing glass to metal (such as for holding glass plates down on to a metal grinding tool or for securing a prism on its table for example). Preferably the parts should be gently warmed and the cement applied hot. It is not particularly hard when set, and on this account it may not be suitable for certain requirements; but its "elasticity" prevents strain occurring if a glass window is cemented on to a metal plate. Its melting point is about 50°C. and a suitable solvent is benzene.

Shellac.

Shellac is the main ingredient of sealing wax, which is of course much used for cementing end-plates to vacuum tubes, but for optical purposes generally the natural orange shellac is preferable on account of its high strength. It can be used in stick form when it is applied with a heated rod, or in thick paste form when it is dissolved in alcohol; both forms have their applications.

Litharge Cement.

A cement which will hold against water, acids and alkalies, suitable for holding glass windows in metal troughs or tanks, can be made by mixing litharge with pure glycerin to the consistency of a paste.

Waterglass Cements.

By mixing waterglass (i.e. sodium silicate) with the carbonates of calcium, zinc or lead, a moist tenacious and hard cement may be formed. In a few hours these mixtures set rock hard.

Zinc Oxychloride.

This cement is frequently used in dental work and again is hard-setting and has considerable adhesive powers. It is particularly good for holding glass-work to metal. It is made from a 60 per cent. zinc chloride solution and zinc oxide powder mixed to the consistency of a thick paste.

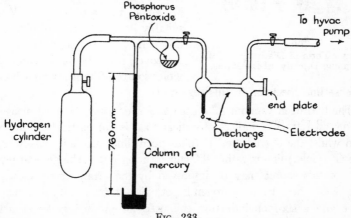

FIG. 233.

Apparatus for giving greater intensity of the Lines in the Hydrogen Spectrum

Sources of Light.

The two most generally employed sources of monochromatic light in the optical laboratory or workshop are the sodium lamp and the mercury lamp. Whilst a Bunsen burner playing on a sodium chloride "brick" is simple and useful for many purposes, much greater intensity is obtained from the sodium electric discharge tube running off the main and is therefore more suitable for interference experiments and tests. For a similar reason, regarding the intensity of the light, the mercury vapour lamp is a distinctly valuable source; moreover, the green, yellow and violet lines can each be used individually as a monochromatic source by utilising suitable filters. Various forms of high- and low-pressure Hg lamps are now made running off the mains in conjunction with a choke, but one of the most compact and hard-working lamps of this series is the Osira (manufactured by the General Electric Company, Wembley). Originally intended as an ultra-violet lamp, the outer dark bulb can be removed, leaving a small silica tube in which the arc occurs. When suitably housed in a small container this makes a very convenient unit; moreover, it can be used as an ultra-violet source of light giving a highly intense line spectrum in this region.

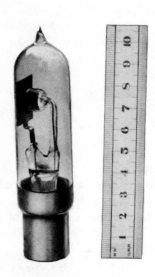

FIG. 234.
Simple Form of Discharge Tube Running Directly off the Mains.

The hydrogen vacuum tube used as a source for standard measurements on refractive indices of optical glass is not particularly intense; and whilst the C (red) and F (blue-green) lines are fairly easily seen, the G′ (violet) line is rather difficult to bring out. The general intensity of this source may be improved by the arrangement shown in Fig. 233, where fresh hydrogen is periodically drawn into the vacuum tube and a six-inch induction coil used for producing the electrical discharge.

Other simple forms of light source which may be run directly off the electrical mains are the small discharge tubes (see Fig. 234) giving emission spectra of various gases, such as oxygen, nitrogen, argon, neon, helium, etc. Whilst they are not useful as high intensity sources they are convenient for giving line spectra when calibrating a spectrometer for example. Neon is particularly useful at the red end of the spectrum.

For producing a continuous spectrum or for optical projection purposes, the 500 C.P. Pointolite lamp (i.e. tungsten arc) is probably the most convenient source, for although it has not the intrinsic brightness of the carbon arc, it is a great deal steadier. Various light filters which cover the whole spectral range in bands of about 400 A.U. can now be obtained and can be used successfully with the above lamp.

TABLE OF USEFUL WAVELENGTHS (VISIBLE SPECTRUM).

Wavelength A.U.	Colour.	Substance.	How emitted.
5890	Yellow.	Sodium.	Bunsen flame or
5896	,,	,,	discharge tube.
6563	Red.	Hydrogen.	Vacuum tube.
4861	Blue-green.	,,	,, ,,
4341	Violet.	,,	,, ,,
5791	Yellow.	Mercury.	Mercury lamp.
5770	,,	,,	,, ,,
5461	Green.	,,	,, ,,
4078	Violet.	,,	,, ,,
7947	Far red.	Rubidium.	On positive pole
7806	,,	,,	of carbon arc.
6708	Red.	Lithium.	,, ,,
3969	Violet.	Calcium.	,, ,,
3934	,,	,,	,, ,,

Sign Convention.

Owing to the fact that there are still a great variety of sign conventions (for use with lens and mirror problems) taught in the schools, it is often found difficult to avoid confusion in the student's mind when a new sign convention (such as that recommended by the Physical Society) is introduced either at the university or in commerce.

The author has found from his experience in teaching large numbers of students that if such confusion does arise, this can be overcome quite readily by getting students to think of a sign convention based solely on the use of the ordinary Cartesian co-ordinates, **without** the proviso of stipulating that the initial direction of progress of the light is the positive direction (see page 25).

If the lens or mirror is then considered as being situated at the origin (see Fig. 31) then distances measured along the axis to the left will be negative and distances to the right positive, in accordance with the **true** Cartesian principle. Although such a system gives a positive focal length to a lens on one side and a negative focal length on the other, it has the advantage that the object may be placed on the right or the left of the lens or mirror as desired, and all the student has to do is to recall the signs of the Cartesian co-ordinates (which are in-ground even in the most elementary mind) and to apply them without having to ask himself (for example) whether a direction is measured **against** or **with** the direction of the incident light or whether such distances are to be reckoned as positive or negative; the Cartesian co-ordinates automatically tell him this.

With such a sign convention it is not necessary to think of a lens or mirror as being called a positive one or a negative one, but rather to think of them in the more natural terms of a convergent or divergent lens or mirror; and when working out examples, simply to give the value f an appropriate sign in the required formula.

The sign of f is also obtained in a perfectly natural manner, for when once the position of the object has been decided on (whether to the left or the right of the lens or mirror) the Cartesian co-ordinates will again tell us the correct sign to allot to the value f.

For example, if the object is on the left, a lens which produces convergence of the light will have a positive sign for the value of f, whereas if the object is situated on the right the same lens will have a negative sign f for use in the formula. On the other hand, if a diverging lens is used, it will have a negative sign for f when the object is on the left and a positive sign if the object is on the right.

Further this system also has the advantage that it is consistent throughout whether applied to lenses or mirrors, whereas some sign conventions provide a negative sign to a **mirror** which produces convergence of the light; this is directly opposite in sign to a **lens** which produces convergence.

This idea, which closely resembles that set out by the late Professor A. E. Conrady, is put forward merely as a suggestion for considered opinion by those who find difficulty in dealing with a subject in which students have been previously trained in various forms of sign convention.

The author has found that the above stated system is readily absorbed, and that it has met with success in dispelling confusion when it has arisen.

INDEX

CATALOGUE OF DOVER BOOKS

PHYSICS

General physics

FOUNDATIONS OF PHYSICS, R. B. Lindsay & H. Margenau. Excellent bridge between semi-popular works & technical treatises. A discussion of methods of physical description, construction of theory; valuable for physicist with elementary calculus who is interested in ideas that give meaning to data, tools of modern physics. Contents include symbolism, mathematical equations; space & time foundations of mechanics; probability; physics & continua; electron theory; special & general relativity; quantum mechanics; causality. "Thorough and yet not overdetailed. Unreservedly recommended," NATURE (London). Unabridged, corrected edition. List of recommended readings. 35 illustrations. xi + 537pp. 5⅜ x 8.
S377 Paperbound **$2.75**

FUNDAMENTAL FORMULAS OF PHYSICS, ed. by D. H. Menzel. Highly useful, fully inexpensive reference and study text, ranging from simple to highly sophisticated operations. Mathematics integrated into text—each chapter stands as short textbook of field represented. Vol. 1: Statistics, Physical Constants, Special Theory of Relativity, Hydrodynamics, Aerodynamics, Boundary Value Problems in Math. Physics; Viscosity, Electromagnetic Theory, etc. Vol. 2: Sound, Acoustics, Geometrical Optics, Electron Optics, High-Energy Phenomena, Magnetism, Biophysics, much more. Index. Total of 800pp. 5⅜ x 8.
Vol. 1 S595 Paperbound **$2.00**
Vol. 2 S596 Paperbound **$2.00**

MATHEMATICAL PHYSICS, D. H. Menzel. Thorough one-volume treatment of the mathematical techniques vital for classic mechanics, electromagnetic theory, quantum theory, and relativity. Written by the Harvard Professor of Astrophysics for junior, senior, and graduate courses, it gives clear explanations of all those aspects of function theory, vectors, matrices, dyadics, tensors, partial differential equations, etc., necessary for the understanding of the various physical theories. Electron theory, relativity, and other topics seldom presented appear here in considerable detail. Scores of definitions, conversion factors, dimensional constants, etc. "More detailed than normal for an advanced text . . . excellent set of sections on Dyadics, Matrices, and Tensors," JOURNAL OF THE FRANKLIN INSTITUTE. Index. 193 problems, with answers. x + 412pp. 5⅜ x 8.
S56 Paperbound **$2.00**

THE SCIENTIFIC PAPERS OF J. WILLARD GIBBS. All the published papers of America's outstanding theoretical scientist (except for "Statistical Mechanics" and "Vector Analysis"). Vol I (thermodynamics) contains one of the most brilliant of all 19th-century scientific papers—the 300-page "On the Equilibrium of Heterogeneous Substances," which founded the science of physical chemistry, and clearly stated a number of highly important natural laws for the first time; 8 other papers complete the first volume. Vol II includes 2 papers on dynamics, 8 on vector analysis and multiple algebra, 5 on the electromagnetic theory of light, and 6 miscellaneous papers. Biographical sketch by H. A. Bumstead. Total of xxxvi + 718pp. 5⅝ x 8⅜.
S721 Vol I Paperbound **$2.50**
S722 Vol II Paperbound **$2.00**
The set **$4.50**

BASIC THEORIES OF PHYSICS, Peter Gabriel Bergmann. Two-volume set which presents a critical examination of important topics in the major subdivisions of classical and modern physics. The first volume is concerned with classical mechanics and electrodynamics: mechanics of mass points, analytical mechanics, matter in bulk, electrostatics and magnetostatics, electromagnetic interaction, the field waves, special relativity, and waves. The second volume (Heat and Quanta) contains discussions of the kinetic hypothesis, physics and statistics, stationary ensembles, laws of thermodynamics, early quantum theories, atomic spectra, probability waves, quantization in wave mechanics, approximation methods, and abstract quantum theory. A valuable supplement to any thorough course or text.
Heat and Quanta: Index. 8 figures. x + 300pp. 5⅜ x 8½.
S968 Paperbound **$1.75**
Mechanics and Electrodynamics: Index. 14 figures. vii + 280pp. 5⅜ x 8½.
S969 Paperbound **$1.75**

THEORETICAL PHYSICS, A. S. Kompaneyets. One of the very few thorough studies of the subject in this price range. Provides advanced students with a comprehensive theoretical background. Especially strong on recent experimentation and developments in quantum theory. Contents: Mechanics (Generalized Coordinates, Lagrange's Equation, Collision of Particles, etc.), Electrodynamics (Vector Analysis, Maxwell's equations, Transmission of Signals, Theory of Relativity, etc.), Quantum Mechanics (the Inadequacy of Classical Mechanics, the Wave Equation, Motion in a Central Field, Quantum Theory of Radiation, Quantum Theories of Dispersion and Scattering, etc.), and Statistical Physics (Equilibrium Distribution of Molecules in an Ideal Gas, Boltzmann statistics, Bose and Fermi Distribution, Thermodynamic Quantities, etc.). Revised to 1961. Translated by George Yankovsky, authorized by Kompaneyets. 137 exercises. 56 figures. 529pp. 5⅜ x 8½. S972 Paperbound **$2.50**

ANALYTICAL AND CANONICAL FORMALISM IN PHYSICS, André Mercier. A survey, in one volume, of the variational principles (the key principles—in mathematical form—from which the basic laws of any one branch of physics can be derived) of the several branches of physical theory, together with an examination of the relationships among them. Contents: the Lagrangian Formalism, Lagrangian Densities, Canonical Formalism, Canonical Form of Electrodynamics, Hamiltonian Densities, Transformations, and Canonical Form with Vanishing Jacobian Determinant. Numerous examples and exercises. For advanced students, teachers, etc. 6 figures. Index. viii + 222pp. 5⅜ x 8½. S1077 Paperbound **$1.75**

Acoustics, optics, electricity and magnetism, electromagnetics, magneto-hydrodynamics

THE THEORY OF SOUND, Lord Rayleigh. Most vibrating systems likely to be encountered in practice can be tackled successfully by the methods set forth by the great Nobel laureate, Lord Rayleigh. Complete coverage of experimental, mathematical aspects of sound theory. Partial contents: Harmonic motions, vibrating systems in general, lateral vibrations of bars, curved plates or shells, applications of Laplace's functions to acoustical problems, fluid friction, plane vortex-sheet, vibrations of solid bodies, etc. This is the first inexpensive edition of this great reference and study work. Bibliography. Historical introduction by R. B. Lindsay. Total of 1040pp. 97 figures. 5⅜ x 8.
S292, S293, Two volume set, paperbound, **$4.70**

THE DYNAMICAL THEORY OF SOUND, H. Lamb. Comprehensive mathematical treatment of the physical aspects of sound, covering the theory of vibrations, the general theory of sound, and the equations of motion of strings, bars, membranes, pipes, and resonators. Includes chapters on plane, spherical, and simple harmonic waves, and the Helmholtz Theory of Audition. Complete and self-contained development for student and specialist; all fundamental differential equations solved completely. Specific mathematical details for such important phenomena as harmonics, normal modes, forced vibrations of strings, theory of reed pipes, etc. Index. Bibliography. 86 diagrams. viii + 307pp. 5⅜ x 8. S655 Paperbound **$1.50**

WAVE PROPAGATION IN PERIODIC STRUCTURES, L. Brillouin. A general method and application to different problems: pure physics, such as scattering of X-rays of crystals, thermal vibration in crystal lattices, electronic motion in metals; and also problems of electrical engineering. Partial contents: elastic waves in 1-dimensional lattices of point masses. Propagation of waves along 1-dimensional lattices. Energy flow. 2 dimensional, 3 dimensional lattices. Mathieu's equation. Matrices and propagation of waves along an electric line. Continuous electric lines. 131 illustrations. Bibliography. Index. xii + 253pp. 5⅜ x 8.
S34 Paperbound **$2.00**

THEORY OF VIBRATIONS, N. W. McLachlan. Based on an exceptionally successful graduate course given at Brown University, this discusses linear systems having 1 degree of freedom, forced vibrations of simple linear systems, vibration of flexible strings, transverse vibrations of bars and tubes, transverse vibration of circular plate, sound waves of finite amplitude, etc. Index. 99 diagrams. 160pp. 5⅜ x 8. S190 Paperbound **$1.35**

LIGHT: PRINCIPLES AND EXPERIMENTS, George S. Monk. Covers theory, experimentation, and research. Intended for students with some background in general physics and elementary calculus. Three main divisions: 1) Eight chapters on geometrical optics—fundamental concepts (the ray and its optical length, Fermat's principle, etc.), laws of image formation, apertures in optical systems, photometry, optical instruments etc.; 2) 9 chapters on physical optics—interference, diffraction, polarization, spectra, the Rayleigh refractometer, the wave theory of light, etc.; 3) 23 instructive experiments based directly on the theoretical text. "Probably the best intermediate textbook on light in the English language. Certainly, it is the best book which includes both geometrical and physical optics," J. Rud Nielson, PHYSICS FORUM. Revised edition. 102 problems and answers. 12 appendices. 6 tables. Index. 270 illustrations. xi +489pp. 5⅜ x 8½. S341 Paperbound **$2.50**

PHOTOMETRY, John W. T. Walsh. The best treatment of both "bench" and "illumination" photometry in English by one of Britain's foremost experts in the field (President of the International Commission on Illumination). Limited to those matters, theoretical and practical, which affect the measurement of light flux, candlepower, illumination, etc., and excludes treatment of the use to which such measurements may be put after they have been made. Chapters on Radiation, The Eye and Vision, Photo-Electric Cells, The Principles of Photometry, The Measurement of Luminous Intensity, Colorimetry, Spectrophotometry, Stellar Photometry, The Photometric Laboratory, etc. Third revised (1958) edition. 281 illustrations. 10 appendices. xxiv + 544pp. 5½ x 9¼. S319 Clothbound **$10.00**

EXPERIMENTAL SPECTROSCOPY, R. A. Sawyer. Clear discussion of prism and grating spectrographs and the techniques of their use in research, with emphasis on those principles and techniques that are fundamental to practically all uses of spectroscopic equipment. Beginning with a brief history of spectroscopy, the author covers such topics as light sources, spectroscopic apparatus, prism spectroscopes and graphs, diffraction grating, the photographic process, determination of wave length, spectral intensity, infrared spectroscopy, spectrochemical analysis, etc. This revised edition contains new material on the production of replica gratings, solar spectroscopy from rockets, new standard of wave length, etc. Index. Bibliography. 111 illustrations. x + 358pp. 5⅜ x 8½. S1045 Paperbound **$2.25**

FUNDAMENTALS OF ELECTRICITY AND MAGNETISM, L. B. Loeb. For students of physics, chemistry, or engineering who want an introduction to electricity and magnetism on a higher level and in more detail than general elementary physics texts provide. Only elementary differential and integral calculus is assumed. Physical laws developed logically, from magnetism to electric currents, Ohm's law, electrolysis, and on to static electricity, induction, etc. Covers an unusual amount of material; one third of book on modern material: solution of wave equation, photoelectric and thermionic effects, etc. Complete statement of the various electrical systems of units and interrelations. 2 Indexes. 75 pages of problems with answers stated. Over 300 figures and diagrams. xix +669pp. 5⅜ x 8. S745 Paperbound **$2.75**

MATHEMATICAL ANALYSIS OF ELECTRICAL AND OPTICAL WAVE-MOTION, Harry Bateman. Written by one of this century's most distinguished mathematical physicists, this is a practical introduction to those developments of Maxwell's electromagnetic theory which are directly connected with the solution of the partial differential equation of wave motion. Methods of solving wave-equation, polar-cylindrical coordinates, diffraction, transformation of coordinates, homogeneous solutions, electromagnetic fields with moving singularities, etc. Index. 168pp. 5⅜ x 8. S14 Paperbound **$1.75**

PRINCIPLES OF PHYSICAL OPTICS, Ernst Mach. This classical examination of the propagation of light, color, polarization, etc. offers an historical and philosophical treatment that has never been surpassed for breadth and easy readability. Contents: Rectilinear propagation of light. Reflection, refraction. Early knowledge of vision. Dioptrics. Composition of light. Theory of color and dispersion. Periodicity. Theory of interference. Polarization. Mathematical representation of properties of light. Propagation of waves, etc. 279 illustrations, 10 portraits. Appendix. Indexes. 324pp. 5⅜ x 8. S178 Paperbound **$2.00**

THE THEORY OF OPTICS, Paul Drude. One of finest fundamental texts in physical optics, classic offers thorough coverage, complete mathematical treatment of basic ideas. Includes fullest treatment of application of thermodynamics to optics; sine law in formation of images, transparent crystals, magnetically active substances, velocity of light, apertures, effects depending upon them, polarization, optical instruments, etc. Introduction by A. A. Michelson. Index. 110 illus. 567pp. 5⅜ x 8. S532 Paperbound **$2.45**

ELECTRICAL THEORY ON THE GIORGI SYSTEM, P. Cornelius. A new clarification of the fundamental concepts of electricity and magnetism, advocating the convenient m.k.s. system of units that is steadily gaining followers in the sciences. Illustrating the use and effectiveness of his terminology with numerous applications to concrete technical problems, the author here expounds the famous Giorgi system of electrical physics. His lucid presentation and well-reasoned, cogent argument for the universal adoption of this system form one of the finest pieces of scientific exposition in recent years. 28 figures. Index. Conversion tables for translating earlier data into modern units. Translated from 3rd Dutch edition by L. J. Jolley. x + 187pp. 5½ x 8¾. S909 Clothbound **$6.00**

ELECTRIC WAVES: BEING RESEARCHES ON THE PROPAGATION OF ELECTRIC ACTION WITH FINITE VELOCITY THROUGH SPACE, Heinrich Hertz. This classic work brings together the original papers in which Hertz—Helmholtz's protegé and one of the most brilliant figures in 19th-century research—probed the existence of electromagnetic waves and showed experimentally that their velocity equalled that of light, research that helped lay the groundwork for the development of radio, television, telephone, telegraph, and other modern technological marvels. Unabridged republication of original edition. Authorized translation by D. E. Jones. Preface by Lord Kelvin. Index of names. 40 illustrations. xvii + 278pp. 5⅜ x 8½. S57 Paperbound **$1.75**

PIEZOELECTRICITY: AN INTRODUCTION TO THE THEORY AND APPLICATIONS OF ELECTRO-MECHANICAL PHENOMENA IN CRYSTALS, Walter G. Cady. This is the most complete and systematic coverage of this important field in print—now regarded as something of scientific classic. This republication, revised and corrected by Prof. Cady—one of the foremost contributors in this area—contains a sketch of recent progress and new material on Ferroelectrics. Time Standards, etc. The first 7 chapters deal with fundamental theory of crystal electricity. 5 important chapters cover basic concepts of piezoelectricity, including comparisons of various competing theories in the field. Also discussed: piezoelectric resonators (theory, methods of manufacture, influences of air-gaps, etc.); the piezo oscillator; the properties, history, and observations relating to Rochelle salt; ferroelectric crystals; miscellaneous applications of piezoelectricity; pyroelectricity; etc. "A great work," W. A. Wooster, NATURE. Revised (1963) and corrected edition. New preface by Prof. Cady. 2 Appendices. Indices. Illustrations. 62 tables. Bibliography. Problems. Total of 1 + 822pp. 5⅜ x 8½.
S1094 Vol. I Paperbound **$2.50**
S1095 Vol. II Paperbound **$2.50**
Two volume set Paperbound **$5.00**

MAGNETISM AND VERY LOW TEMPERATURES, H. B. G. Casimir. A basic work in the literature of low temperature physics. Presents a concise survey of fundamental theoretical principles, and also points out promising lines of investigation. Contents: Classical Theory and Experimental Methods, Quantum Theory of Paramagnetism, Experiments on Adiabatic Demagnetization. Theoretical Discussion of Paramagnetism at Very Low Temperatures, Some Experimental Results, Relaxation Phenomena. Index. 89-item bibliography. ix + 95pp. 5⅜ x 8. S943 Paperbound **$1.25**

SELECTED PAPERS ON NEW TECHNIQUES FOR ENERGY CONVERSION: THERMOELECTRIC METHODS; THERMIONIC; PHOTOVOLTAIC AND ELECTRICAL EFFECTS; FUSION, Edited by Sumner N. Levine. Brings together in one volume the most important papers (1954-1961) in modern energy technology. Included among the 37 papers are general and qualitative descriptions of the field as a whole, indicating promising lines of research. Also: 15 papers on thermoelectric methods, 7 on thermionic, 5 on photovoltaic, 4 on electrochemical effect, and 2 on controlled fusion research. Among the contributors are: Joffe, Maria Telkes, Herold, Herring, Douglas, Jaumot, Post, Austin, Wilson, Pfann, Rappaport, Morehouse, Domenicali, Moss, Bowers, Harman, Von Doenhoef. Preface and introduction by the editor. Bibliographies. xxviii + 451pp. 6⅛ x 9¼. S37 Paperbound **$3.00**

SUPERFLUIDS: MACROSCOPIC THEORY OF SUPERCONDUCTIVITY, Vol. I, Fritz London. The major work by one of the founders and great theoreticians of modern quantum physics. Consolidates the researches that led to the present understanding of the nature of superconductivity. Prof. London here reveals that quantum mechanics is operative on the macroscopic plane as well as the submolecular level. Contents: Properties of Superconductors and Their Thermodynamical Correlation; Electrodynamics of the Pure Superconducting State; Relation between Current and Field; Measurements of the Penetration Depth; Non-Viscous Flow vs. Superconductivity; Micro-waves in Superconductors; Reality of the Domain Structure; and many other related topics. A new epilogue by M. J. Buckingham discusses developments in the field up to 1960. Corrected and expanded edition. An appreciation of the author's life and work by L. W. Nordheim. Biography by Edith London. Bibliography of his publications. 45 figures. 2 Indices. xviii + 173pp. 5⅝ x 8⅜. **S44 Paperbound $1.45**

SELECTED PAPERS ON PHYSICAL PROCESSES IN IONIZED PLASMAS, Edited by Donald H. Menzel, Director, Harvard College Observatory. 30 important papers relating to the study of highly ionized gases or plasmas selected by a foremost contributor in the field, with the assistance of Dr. L. H. Aller. The essays include 18 on the physical processes in gaseous nebulae, covering problems of radiation and radiative transfer, the Balmer decrement, electron temperatures, spectrophotometry, etc. 10 papers deal with the interpretation of nebular spectra, by Bohm, Van Vleck, Aller, Minkowski, etc. There is also a discussion of the intensities of "forbidden" spectral lines by George Shortley and a paper concerning the theory of hydrogenic spectra by Menzel and Pekeris. Other contributors: Goldberg, Hebb, Baker, Bowen, Ufford, Liller, etc. viii + 374pp. 6⅛ x 9¼. **S60 Paperbound $2.95**

THE ELECTROMAGNETIC FIELD, Max Mason & Warren Weaver. Used constantly by graduate engineers. Vector methods exclusively: detailed treatment of electrostatics, expansion methods, with tables converting any quantity into absolute electromagnetic, absolute electrostatic, practical units. Discrete charges, ponderable bodies, Maxwell field equations, etc. Introduction. Indexes. 416pp. 5⅜ x 8. **S185 Paperbound $2.00**

THEORY OF ELECTRONS AND ITS APPLICATION TO THE PHENOMENA OF LIGHT AND RADIANT HEAT, H. Lorentz. Lectures delivered at Columbia University by Nobel laureate Lorentz. Unabridged, they form a historical coverage of the theory of free electrons, motion, absorption of heat, Zeeman effect, propagation of light in molecular bodies, inverse Zeeman effect, optical phenomena in moving bodies, etc. 109 pages of notes explain the more advanced sections. Index. 9 figures. 352pp. 5⅜ x 8. **S173 Paperbound $1.85**

FUNDAMENTAL ELECTROMAGNETIC THEORY, Ronold P. King, Professor Applied Physics, Harvard University. Original and valuable introduction to electromagnetic theory and to circuit theory from the standpoint of electromagnetic theory. Contents: Mathematical Description of Matter—stationary and nonstationary states; Mathematical Description of Space and of Simple Media—Field Equations, Integral Forms of Field Equations, Electromagnetic Force, etc.; Transformation of Field and Force Equations; Electromagnetic Waves in Unbounded Regions; Skin Effect and Internal Impedance—in a solid cylindrical conductor, etc.; and Electrical Circuits—Analytical Foundations, Near-zone and quasi-near zone circuits, Balanced two-wire and four-wire transmission lines. Revised and enlarged version. New preface by the author. 5 appendices (Differential operators: Vector Formulas and Identities, etc.). Problems. Indexes. Bibliography. xvi + 580pp. 5⅜ x 8½. **S1023 Paperbound $2.75**

Hydrodynamics

A TREATISE ON HYDRODYNAMICS, A. B. Basset. Favorite text on hydrodynamics for 2 generations of physicists, hydrodynamical engineers, oceanographers, ship designers, etc. Clear enough for the beginning student, and thorough source for graduate students and engineers on the work of d'Alembert, Euler, Laplace, Lagrange, Poisson, Green, Clebsch, Stokes, Cauchy, Helmholtz, J. J. Thomson, Love, Hicks, Greenhill, Besant, Lamb, etc. Great amount of documentation on entire theory of classical hydrodynamics. Vol I: theory of motion of frictionless liquids, vortex, and cyclic irrotational motion, etc. 132 exercises. Bibliography. 3 Appendixes. xii + 264pp. Vol II: motion in viscous liquids, harmonic analysis, theory of tides, etc. 112 exercises, Bibliography. 4 Appendixes. xv + 328pp. Two volume set. 5⅜ x 8.
S724 Vol I Paperbound $1.75
S725 Vol II Paperbound $1.75
The set $3.50

HYDRODYNAMICS, Horace Lamb. Internationally famous complete coverage of standard reference work on dynamics of liquids & gases. Fundamental theorems, equations, methods, solutions, background, for classical hydrodynamics. Chapters include Equations of Motion, Integration of Equations in Special Gases, Irrotational Motion, Motion of Liquid in 2 Dimensions, Motion of Solids through Liquid-Dynamical Theory, Vortex Motion, Tidal Waves, Surface Waves, Waves of Expansion, Viscosity, Rotating Masses of liquids. Excellently planned, arranged; clear, lucid presentation. 6th enlarged, revised edition. Index. Over 900 footnotes, mostly bibliographical. 119 figures. xv + 738pp. 6⅛ x 9¼. **S256 Paperbound $3.75**

HYDRODYNAMICS, H. Dryden, F. Murnaghan, Harry Bateman. Published by the National Research Council in 1932 this enormous volume offers a complete coverage of classical hydrodynamics. Encyclopedic in quality. Partial contents: physics of fluids, motion, turbulent flow, compressible fluids, motion in 1, 2, 3 dimensions; viscous fluids rotating, laminar motion, resistance of motion through viscous fluid, eddy viscosity, hydraulic flow in channels of various shapes, discharge of gases, flow past obstacles, etc. Bibliography of over 2,900 items. Indexes. 23 figures. 634pp. 5⅜ x 8. S303 Paperbound **$2.75**

Mechanics, dynamics, thermodynamics, elasticity

MECHANICS, J. P. Den Hartog. Already a classic among introductory texts, the M.I.T. professor's lively and discursive presentation is equally valuable as a beginner's text, an engineering student's refresher, or a practicing engineer's reference. Emphasis in this highly readable text is on illuminating fundamental principles and showing how they are embodied in a great number of real engineering and design problems: trusses, loaded cables, beams, jacks, hoists, etc. Provides advanced material on relative motion and gyroscopes not usual in introductory texts. "Very thoroughly recommended to all those anxious to improve their real understanding of the principles of mechanics." MECHANICAL WORLD. Index. List of equations. 334 problems, all with answers. Over 550 diagrams and drawings. ix + 462pp. 5⅜ x 8. S754 Paperbound **$2.00**

THEORETICAL MECHANICS: AN INTRODUCTION TO MATHEMATICAL PHYSICS, J. S. Ames, F. D. Murnaghan. A mathematically rigorous development of theoretical mechanics for the advanced student, with constant practical applications. Used in hundreds of advanced courses. An unusually thorough coverage of gyroscopic and baryscopic material, detailed analyses of the Coriolis acceleration, applications of Lagrange's equations, motion of the double pendulum, Hamilton-Jacobi partial differential equations, group velocity and dispersion, etc. Special relativity is also included. 159 problems. 44 figures. ix + 462pp. 5⅜ x 8. S461 Paperbound **$2.25**

THEORETICAL MECHANICS: STATICS AND THE DYNAMICS OF A PARTICLE, W. D. MacMillan. Used for over 3 decades as a self-contained and extremely comprehensive advanced undergraduate text in mathematical physics, physics, astronomy, and deeper foundations of engineering. Early sections require only a knowledge of geometry; later, a working knowledge of calculus. Hundreds of basic problems, including projectiles to the moon, escape velocity, harmonic motion, ballistics, falling bodies, transmission of power, stress and strain, elasticity, astronomical problems. 340 practice problems plus many fully worked out examples make it possible to test and extend principles developed in the text. 200 figures. xvii + 430pp. 5⅜ x 8. S467 Paperbound **$2.00**

THEORETICAL MECHANICS: THE THEORY OF THE POTENTIAL, W. D. MacMillan. A comprehensive, well balanced presentation of potential theory, serving both as an introduction and a reference work with regard to specific problems, for physicists and mathematicians. No prior knowledge of integral relations is assumed, and all mathematical material is developed as it becomes necessary. Includes: Attraction of Finite Bodies; Newtonian Potential Function; Vector Fields, Green and Gauss Theorems; Attractions of Surfaces and Lines; Surface Distribution of Matter; Two-Layer Surfaces; Spherical Harmonics; Ellipsoidal Harmonics; etc. "The great number of particular cases . . . should make the book valuable to geophysicists and others actively engaged in practical applications of the potential theory," Review of Scientific Instruments. Index. Bibliography. xiii + 469pp. 5⅜ x 8. S486 Paperbound **$2.25**

THEORETICAL MECHANICS: DYNAMICS OF RIGID BODIES, W. D. MacMillan. Theory of dynamics of a rigid body is developed, using both the geometrical and analytical methods of instruction. Begins with exposition of algebra of vectors, it goes through momentum principles, motion in space, use of differential equations and infinite series to solve more sophisticated dynamics problems. Partial contents: moments of inertia, systems of free particles, motion parallel to a fixed plane, rolling motion, method of periodic solutions, much more. 82 figs. 199 problems. Bibliography. Indexes. xii + 476pp. 5⅜ x 8. S641 Paperbound **$2.00**

MATHEMATICAL FOUNDATIONS OF STATISTICAL MECHANICS, A. I. Khinchin. Offering a precise and rigorous formulation of problems, this book supplies a thorough and up-to-date exposition. It provides analytical tools needed to replace cumbersome concepts, and furnishes for the first time a logical step-by-step introduction to the subject. Partial contents: geometry & kinematics of the phase space, ergodic problem, reduction to theory of probability, application of central limit problem, ideal monatomic gas, foundation of thermo-dynamics, dispersion and distribution of sum functions. Key to notations. Index. viii + 179pp. 5⅜ x 8. S147 Paperbound **$1.50**

ELEMENTARY PRINCIPLES IN STATISTICAL MECHANICS, J. W. Gibbs. Last work of the great Yale mathematical physicist, still one of the most fundamental treatments available for advanced students and workers in the field. Covers the basic principle of conservation of probability of phase, theory of errors in the calculated phases of a system, the contributions of Clausius, Maxwell, Boltzmann, and Gibbs himself, and much more. Includes valuable comparison of statistical mechanics with thermodynamics: Carnot's cycle, mechanical definitions of entropy, etc. xvi + 208pp. 5⅜ x 8. S707 Paperbound **$1.45**

PRINCIPLES OF MECHANICS AND DYNAMICS, Sir William Thomson (Lord Kelvin) and Peter Guthrie Tait. The principles and theories of fundamental branches of classical physics explained by two of the greatest physicists of all time. A broad survey of mechanics, with material on hydrodynamics, elasticity, potential theory, and what is now standard mechanics. Thorough and detailed coverage, with many examples, derivations, and topics not included in more recent studies. Only a knowledge of calculus is needed to work through this book. Vol. I (Preliminary): Kinematics; Dynamical Laws and · Principles; Experience (observation, experimentation, formation of hypotheses, scientific method); Measures and Instruments; Continuous Calculating Machines. Vol. II (Abstract Dynamics): Statics of a Particle—Attraction; Statics of Solids and Fluids. Formerly Titled "Treatise on Natural Philosophy." Unabridged reprint of revised edition. Index. 168 diagrams. Total of xlii + 1035pp. 5⅜ x 8½.

Vol. I: S966 Paperbound **$2.35**
Vol. II: S967 Paperbound **$2.35**
Two volume Set Paperbound **$4.70**

INVESTIGATIONS ON THE THEORY OF THE BROWNIAN MOVEMENT, Albert Einstein. Reprints from rare European journals. 5 basic papers, including the Elementary Theory of the Brownian Movement, written at the request of Lorentz to provide a simple explanation. Translated by A. D. Cowper. Annotated, edited by R. Fürth. 33pp. of notes elucidate, give history of previous investigations. Author, subject indexes. 62 footnotes. 124pp. 5⅜ x 8.

S304 Paperbound **$1.25**

MECHANICS VIA THE CALCULUS, P. W. Norris, W. S. Legge. Covers almost everything, from linear motion to vector analysis: equations determining motion, linear methods, compounding of simple harmonic motions, Newton's laws of motion, Hooke's law, the simple pendulum, motion of a particle in 1 plane, centers of gravity, virtual work, friction, kinetic energy of rotating bodies, equilibrium of strings, hydrostatics, sheering stresses, elasticity, etc. 550 problems. 3rd revised edition. xii + 367pp. 6 x 9.

S207 Clothbound **$4.95**

THE DYNAMICS OF PARTICLES AND OF RIGID, ELASTIC, AND FLUID BODIES; BEING LECTURES ON MATHEMATICAL PHYSICS, A. G. Webster. The reissuing of this classic fills the need for a comprehensive work on dynamics. A wide range of topics is covered in unusually great depth, applying ordinary and partial differential equations. Part I considers laws of motion and methods applicable to systems of all sorts; oscillation, resonance, cyclic systems, etc. Part 2 is a detailed study of the dynamics of rigid bodies. Part 3 introduces the theory of potential; stress and strain, Newtonian potential functions, gyrostatics, wave and vortex motion, etc. Further contents: Kinematics of a point; Lagrange's equations; Hamilton's principle; Systems of vectors; Statics and dynamics of deformable bodies; much more, not easily found together in one volume. Unabridged reprinting of 2nd edition. 20 pages of notes on differential equations and the higher analysis. 203 illustrations. Selected bibliography. Index. xi + 588pp. 5⅜ x 8.

S522 Paperbound **$2.45**

A TREATISE ON DYNAMICS OF A PARTICLE, E. J. Routh. Elementary text on dynamics for beginning mathematics or physics student. Unusually detailed treatment from elementary definitions to motion in 3 dimensions, emphasizing concrete aspects. Much unique material important in recent applications. Covers impulsive forces, rectilinear and constrained motion in 2 dimensions, harmonic and parabolic motion, degrees of freedom, closed orbits, the conical pendulum, the principle of least action, Jacobi's method, and much more. Index. 559 problems, many fully worked out, incorporated into text. xiii + 418pp. 5⅜ x 8.

S696 Paperbound **$2.25**

DYNAMICS OF A SYSTEM OF RIGID BODIES (Elementary Section), E. J. Routh. Revised 7th edition of this standard reference. This volume covers the dynamical principles of the subject, and its more elementary applications: finding moments of inertia by integration, foci of inertia, d'Alembert's principle, impulsive forces, motion in 2 and 3 dimensions, Lagrange's equations, relative indicatrix, Euler's theorem, large tautochronous motions, etc. Index. 55 figures. Scores of problems. xv + 443pp. 5⅜ x 8.

S664 Paperbound **$2.50**

DYNAMICS OF A SYSTEM OF RIGID BODIES (Advanced Section), E. J. Routh. Revised 6th edition of a classic reference aid. Much of its material remains unique. Partial contents: moving axes, relative motion, oscillations about equilibrium, motion. Motion of a body under no forces, any forces. Nature of motion given by linear equations and conditions of stability. Free, forced vibrations, constants of integration, calculus of finite differences, variations, precession and nutation, motion of the moon, motion of string, chain, membranes. 64 figures. 498pp. 5⅜ x 8.

S229 Paperbound **$2.45**

DYNAMICAL THEORY OF GASES, James Jeans. Divided into mathematical and physical chapters for the convenience of those not expert in mathematics, this volume discusses the mathematical theory of gas in a steady state, thermodynamics, Boltzmann and Maxwell, kinetic theory, quantum theory, exponentials, etc. 4th enlarged edition, with new material on quantum theory, quantum dynamics, etc. Indexes. 28 figures. 444pp. 6⅛ x 9¼.

S136 Paperbound **$2.65**

THE THEORY OF HEAT RADIATION, Max Planck. A pioneering work in thermodynamics, providing basis for most later work, Nobel laureate Planck writes on Deductions from Electrodynamics and Thermodynamics, Entropy and Probability, Irreversible Radiation Processes, etc. Starts with simple experimental laws of optics, advances to problems of spectral distribution of energy and irreversibility. Bibliography. 7 illustrations, xiv + 224pp. 5⅜ x 8.

S546 Paperbound **$1.50**

FOUNDATIONS OF POTENTIAL THEORY, O. D. Kellogg. Based on courses given at Harvard this is suitable for both advanced and beginning mathematicians. Proofs are rigorous, and much material not generally avaliable elsewhere is included. Partial contents: forces of gravity, fields of force, divergence theorem, properties of Newtonian potentials at points of free space, potentials as solutions of Laplace's equations, harmonic functions, electrostatics, electric images, logarithmic potential, etc. One of Grundlehren Series. ix + 384pp. 5⅜ x 8.
S144 Paperbound **$1.98**

THERMODYNAMICS, Enrico Fermi. Unabridged reproduction of 1937 edition. Elementary in treatment; remarkable for clarity, organization. Requires no knowledge of advanced math beyond calculus, only familiarity with fundamentals of thermometry, calorimetry. Partial Contents: Thermodynamic systems; First & Second laws of thermodynamics; Entropy; Thermodynamic potentials: phase rule, reversible electric cell; Gaseous reactions: van't Hoff reaction box, principle of LeChatelier; Thermodynamics of dilute solutions: osmotic & vapor pressures, boiling & freezing points; Entropy constant. Index. 25 problems. 24 illustrations. x + 160pp. 5⅜ x 8.
S361 Paperbound **$1.75**

THE THERMODYNAMICS OF ELECTRICAL PHENOMENA IN METALS and A CONDENSED COLLECTION OF THERMODYNAMIC FORMULAS, P. W. Bridgman. Major work by the Nobel Prizewinner: stimulating conceptual introduction to aspects of the electron theory of metals, giving an intuitive understanding of fundamental relationships concealed by the formal systems of Onsager and others. Elementary mathematical formulations show clearly the fundamental thermodynamical relationships of the electric field, and a complete phenomenological theory of metals is created. This is the work in which Bridgman announced his famous "thermomotive force" and his distinction between "driving" and "working" electromotive force. We have added in this Dover edition the author's long unavailable tables of thermodynamic formulas, extremely valuable for the speed of reference they allow. Two works bound as one. Index. 33 figures. Bibliography. xviii + 256pp. 5⅜ x 8. S723 Paperbound **$1.65**

TREATISE ON THERMODYNAMICS, Max Planck. Based on Planck's original papers this offers a uniform point of view for the entire field and has been used as an introduction for students who have studied elementary chemistry, physics, and calculus. Rejecting the earlier approaches of Helmholtz and Maxwell, the author makes no assumptions regarding the nature of heat, but begins with a few empirical facts, and from these deduces new physical and chemical laws. 3rd English edition of this standard text by a Nobel laureate. xvi + 297pp. 5⅜ x 8.
S219 Paperbound **$1.75**

THE MATHEMATICAL THEORY OF ELASTICITY, A. E. H. Love. A wealth of practical illustration combined with thorough discussion of fundamentals—theory, application, special problems and solutions. Partial Contents: Analysis of Strain & Stress, Elasticity of Solid Bodies, Elasticity of Crystals, Vibration of Spheres, Cylinders, Propagation of Waves in Elastic Solid Media, Torsion, Theory of Continuous Beams, Plates. Rigorous treatment of Volterra's theory of dislocations, 2-dimensional elastic systems, other topics of modern interest. "For years the standard treatise on elasticity," AMERICAN MATHEMATICAL MONTHLY. 4th revised edition. Index. 76 figures. xviii + 643pp. 6⅛ x 9¼. S174 Paperbound **$3.00**

STRESS WAVES IN SOLIDS, H. Kolsky, Professor of Applied Physics, Brown University. The most readable survey of the theoretical core of current knowledge about the propagation of waves in solids, fully correlated with experimental research. Contents: Part I—Elastic Waves: propagation in an extended plastic medium, propagation in bounded elastic media, experimental investigations with elastic materials. Part II—Stress Waves in Imperfectly Elastic Media: internal friction, experimental investigations of dynamic elastic properties, plastic waves and shock waves, fractures produced by stress waves. List of symbols. Appendix. Supplemented bibliography. 3 full-page plates. 46 figures. x + 213pp. 5⅜ x 8½.
S1098 Paperbound **$1.55**

Relativity, quantum theory, atomic and nuclear physics

SPACE TIME MATTER, Hermann Weyl. "The standard treatise on the general theory of relativity" (Nature), written by a world-renowned scientist, provides a deep clear discussion of the logical coherence of the general theory, with introduction to all the mathematical tools needed: Maxwell, analytical geometry, non-Euclidean geometry, tensor calculus, etc. Basis is classical space-time, before absorption of relativity. Partial contents: Euclidean space, mathematical form, metrical continuum, relativity of time and space, general theory. 15 diagrams. Bibliography. New preface for this edition. xviii + 330pp. 5⅜ x 8.
S267 Paperbound **$2.00**

ATOMIC SPECTRA AND ATOMIC STRUCTURE, G. Herzberg. Excellent general survey for chemists, physicists specializing in other fields. Partial contents: simplest line spectra and elements of atomic theory, building-up principle and periodic system of elements, hyperfine structure of spectral lines, some experiments and applications. Bibliography. 80 figures. Index. xii + 257pp. 5⅜ x 8.
S115 Paperbound **$2.00**

THE PRINCIPLE OF RELATIVITY, A. Einstein, H. Lorentz, H. Minkowski, H. Weyl. These are the 11 basic papers that founded the general and special theories of relativity, all translated into English. Two papers by Lorentz on the Michelson experiment, electromagnetic phenomena. Minkowski's SPACE & TIME, and Weyl's GRAVITATION & ELECTRICITY. 7 epoch-making papers by Einstein: ELECTROMAGNETICS OF MOVING BODIES, INFLUENCE OF GRAVITATION IN PROPAGATION OF LIGHT, COSMOLOGICAL CONSIDERATIONS, GENERAL THEORY, and 3 others. 7 diagrams. Special notes by A. Sommerfeld. 224pp. 5⅜ x 8.
S81 Paperbound **$1.75**

EINSTEIN'S THEORY OF RELATIVITY, Max Born. Revised edition prepared with the collaboration of Gunther Leibfried and Walter Biem. Steering a middle course between superficial popularizations and complex analyses, a Nobel laureate explains Einstein's theories clearly and with special insight. Easily followed by the layman with a knowledge of high school mathematics, the book has been thoroughly revised and extended to modernize those sections of the well-known original edition which are now out of date. After a comprehensive review of classical physics, Born's discussion of special and general theories of relativity covers such topics as simultaneity, kinematics, Einstein's mechanics and dynamics, relativity of arbitrary motions, the geometry of curved surfaces, the space-time continuum, and many others. Index. Illustrations, vii + 376pp. 5⅜ x 8.
S769 Paperbound **$2.00**

ATOMS, MOLECULES AND QUANTA, Arthur E. Ruark and Harold C. Urey. Revised (1963) and corrected edition of a work that has been a favorite with physics students and teachers for more than 30 years. No other work offers the same combination of atomic structure and molecular physics and of experiment and theory. The first 14 chapters deal with the origins and major experimental data of quantum theory and with the development of conceptions of atomic and molecular structure prior to the new mechanics. These sections provide a thorough introduction to atomic and molecular theory, and are presented lucidly and as simply as possible. The six subsequent chapters are devoted to the laws and basic ideas of quantum mechanics: Wave Mechanics, Hydrogenic Atoms in Wave Mechanics, Matrix Mechanics, General Theory of Quantum Dynamics, etc. For advanced college and graduate students in physics. Revised, corrected republication of original edition, with supplementary notes by the authors. New preface by the authors. 9 appendices. General reference list. Indices. 228 figures. 71 tables. Bibliographical material in notes, etc. Total of xxiii + 810pp. 5⅜ x 8⅜.
S1106 Vol. I Paperbound **$2.50**
S1107 Vol. II Paperbound **$2.50**
Two volume set Paperbound **$5.00**

WAVE MECHANICS AND ITS APPLICATIONS, N. F. Mott and I. N. Sneddon. A comprehensive introduction to the theory of quantum mechanics; not a rigorous mathematical exposition as it progresses, instead, in accordance with the physical problems considered. Many topics difficult to find at the elementary level are discussed in this book. Includes such matters as: the wave nature of matter, the wave equation of Schrödinger, the concept of stationary states, properties of the wave functions, effect of a magnetic field on the energy levels of atoms, electronic spin, two-body problem, theory of solids, cohesive forces in ionic crystals, collision problems, interaction of radiation with matter, relativistic quantum mechanics, etc. All are treated both physically and mathematically. 68 illustrations. 11 tables. Indexes. xii + 393pp. 5⅜ x 8½.
S1070 Paperbound **$2.25**

BASIC METHODS IN TRANSFER PROBLEMS, V. Kourganoff, Professor of Astrophysics, U. of Paris. A coherent digest of all the known methods which can be used for approximate or exact solutions of transfer problems. All methods demonstrated on one particular problem —Milne's problem for a plane parallel medium. Three main sections: fundamental concepts (the radiation field and its interaction with matter, the absorption and emission coefficients, etc.); different methods by which transfer problems can be attacked; and a more general problem—the non-grey case of Milne's problem. Much new material, drawing upon declassified atomic energy reports and data from the USSR. Entirely understandable to the student with a reasonable knowledge of analysis. Unabridged, revised reprinting. New preface by the author. Index. Bibliography. 2 appendices. xv + 281pp. 5⅜ x 8½.
S1074 Paperbound **$2.00**

PRINCIPLES OF QUANTUM MECHANICS, W. V. Houston. Enables student with working knowledge of elementary mathematical physics to develop facility in use of quantum mechanics, understand published work in field. Formulates quantum mechanics in terms of Schroedinger's wave mechanics. Studies evidence for quantum theory, for inadequacy of classical mechanics, 2 postulates of quantum mechanics; numerous important, fruitful applications of quantum mechanics in spectroscopy, collision problems, electrons in solids; other topics. "One of the most rewarding features . . . is the interlacing of problems with text," Amer. J. of Physics. Corrected edition. 21 illus. Index. 296pp. 5⅜ x 8. S524 Paperbound **$1.85**

PHYSICAL PRINCIPLES OF THE QUANTUM THEORY, Werner Heisenberg. A Nobel laureate discusses quantum theory; Heisenberg's own work, Compton, Schroedinger, Wilson, Einstein, many others. Written for physicists, chemists who are not specialists in quantum theory, only elementary formulae are considered in the text; there is a mathematical appendix for specialists. Profound without sacrifice of clarity. Translated by C. Eckart, F. Hoyt. 18 figures. 192pp. 5⅜ x 8. S113 Paperbound **$1.25**

PHYSICS, HISTORIES AND CLASSICS

A HISTORY OF PHYSICS: IN ITS ELEMENTARY BRANCHES (THROUGH 1925), INCLUDING THE EVOLUTION OF PHYSICAL LABORATORIES, Florian Cajori. Revised and enlarged edition. The only first-rate brief history of physics. Still the best entry for a student or teacher into the antecedents of modern theories of physics. A clear, non-mathematical, handy reference work which traces in critical fashion the developments of ideas, theories, techniques, and apparatus from the Greeks to the 1920's. Within each period he analyzes the basic topics of mechanics, light, electricity and magnetism, sound, atomic theory and structure of matter, radioactivity, etc. A chapter on modern research: Curie, Kelvin, Planck's quantum theory, thermodynamics, Fitzgerald and Lorentz, special and general relativity, J. J. Thomson's model of an atom, Bohr's discoveries and later results, wave mechanics, and many other matters. Much bibliographic detail in footnotes. Index. 16 figures. xv + 424pp. 5⅜ x 8. T970 Paperbound **$2.00**

A HISTORY OF THE MATHEMATICAL THEORIES OF ATTRACTION AND THE FIGURE OF THE EARTH: FROM THE TIME OF NEWTON TO THAT OF LAPLACE, I. Todhunter. A technical and detailed review of the theories concerning the shape of the earth and its gravitational pull, from the earliest investigations in the seventeenth century up to the middle of the nineteenth. Some of the greatest mathematicians and scientists in history applied themselves to these questions: Newton ("Principia Mathematica"), Huygens, Maupertuis, Simpson, d'Alembert, etc. Others discussed are Poisson, Gauss, Plana, Lagrange, Boit, and many more. Particular emphasis is placed on the theories of Laplace and Legendre, several chapters being devoted to Laplace's "Mécanique Céleste" and his memoirs, and several others to the memoirs of Legendre. Important to historians of science and mathematics and to the specialist who desires background information in the field. 2 volumes bound as 1. Index. xxxvi + 984pp. 5⅜ x 8.
S148 Clothbound **$7.50**

OPTICKS, Sir Isaac Newton. In its discussions of light, reflection, color, refraction, theories of wave and corpuscular theories of light, this work is packed with scores of insights and discoveries. In its precise and practical discussion of construction of optical apparatus, contemporary understandings of phenomena it is truly fascinating to modern physicists, astronomers, mathematicians. Foreword by Albert Einstein. Preface by I. B. Cohen of Harvard University. 7 pages of portraits, facsimile pages, letters, etc. cxvi + 414pp. 5⅜ x 8.
S205 Paperbound **$2.25**

TREATISE ON LIGHT, Christiaan Huygens. The famous original formulation of the wave theory of light, this readable book is one of the two decisive and definitive works in the field of light (Newton's "Optics" is the other). A scientific giant whose researches ranged over mathematics, astronomy, and physics, Huygens, in this historic work, covers such topics as rays propagated in straight lines, reflection and refraction, the spreading and velocity of light, the nature of opaque bodies, the non-spherical nature of light in the atmosphere, properties of Iceland Crystal, and other related matters. Unabridged republication of original (1912) English edition. Translated and introduced by Silvanus P. Thompson. 52 illustrations. xii + 129pp. 5⅜ x 8.
S179 Paperbound **$1.35**

FARADAY'S EXPERIMENTAL RESEARCHES IN ELECTRICITY. Faraday's historic series of papers containing the fruits of years of original experimentation in electrical theory and electrochemistry. Covers his findings in a variety of areas: Induction of electric currents, Evolution of electricity from magnetism, New electrical state or condition of matter, Explication of Arago's magnetic phenomena, New law of electric conduction, Electro-chemical decomposition, Electricity of the Voltaic Pile, Static Induction, Nature of the electric force or forces, Nature of electric current, The character and direction of the electric force of the Gymnotus, Magneto-electric spark, The magnetization of light and the illumination of magnetic lines of force, The possible relation of gravity to electricity, Sub-terraneous electrotelegraph wires, Some points of magnetic philosophy, The diamagnetic conditions of flame and gases, and many other matters. Complete and unabridged republication. 3 vols. bound as 2. Originally reprinted from the Philosophical Transactions of 1831-8. Indices. Illustrations. Total of 1463pp. 5⅜ x 8.
S783-4, Clothbound **$17.50** (tentative)

REFLECTIONS ON THE MOTIVE POWER OF FIRE, Sadi Carnot, and other papers on the 2nd law of thermodynamics by E. Clapeyron and R. Clausius. Carnot's "Reflections" laid the groundwork of modern thermodynamics. Its non-technical, mostly verbal statements examine the relations between heat and the work done by heat in engines, establishing conditions for the economical working of these engines. The papers by Clapeyron and Clausius here reprinted added further refinements to Carnot's work, and led to its final acceptance by physicists. Selections from posthumous manuscripts of Carnot are also included. All papers in English. New introduction by E. Mendoza. 12 illustrations. xxii + 152pp. 5⅜ x 8.
S661 Paperbound **$1.50**

DIALOGUES CONCERNING TWO NEW SCIENCES, Galileo Galilei. This classic of experimental science, mechanics, engineering, is as enjoyable as it is important. A great historical document giving insights into one of the world's most original thinkers, it is based on 30 years' experimentation. It offers a lively exposition of dynamics, elasticity, sound, ballistics, strength of materials, the scientific method. "Superior to everything else of mine," Galileo. Trans. by H. Crew, A. Salvio. 126 diagrams. Index. xxi + 288pp. 5⅜ x 8.
S99 Paperbound **$1.75**

TREATISE ON ELECTRICITY AND MAGNETISM, James Clerk Maxwell. For more than 80 years a seemingly inexhaustible source of leads for physicists, mathematicians, engineers. Total of 1082pp. on such topics as Measurement of Quantities, Electrostatics, Elementary Mathematical Theory of Electricity, Electrical Work and Energy in a System of Conductors, General Theorems, Theory of Electrical Images, Electrolysis, Conduction, Polarization, Dielectrics, Resistance, etc. "The greatest mathematical physicist since Newton," Sir James Jeans. 3rd edition. 107 figures, 21 plates. 1082pp. 5⅜ x 8.   S636-7, 2 volume set, paperbound **$4.00**

A HISTORY OF THE THEORY OF ELASTICITY AND THE STRENGTH OF MATERIALS, I. Todhunter and K. Pearson. For over 60 years a basic reference, unsurpassed in scope or authority. Both a history of the mathematical theory of elasticity from Galileo, Hooke, and Mariotte to Saint Venant, Kirchhoff, Clebsch, and Lord Kelvin and a detailed presentation of every important mathematical contribution during this period. Presents proofs of thousands of theorems and laws, summarizes every relevant treatise, many unavailable elsewhere. Practically a book apiece is devoted to modern founders: Saint Venant, Lamé, Boussinesq, Rankine, Lord Kelvin, F. Neumann, Kirchhoff, Clebsch. Hundreds of pages of technical and physical treatises on specific applications of elasticity to particular materials. Indispensable for the mathematician, physicist, or engineer working with elasticity. Unabridged, corrected reprint of original 3-volume 1886-1893 edition. Three volume set. Two indexes. Appendix to Vol. I. Total of 2344pp. 5⅜ x 8⅜.   S914–916 The set, Clothbound **$15.00**

DE MAGNETE, William Gilbert. This classic work on magnetism founded a new science. Gilbert was the first to use the word "electricity", to recognize mass as distinct from weight, to discover the effect of heat on magnetic bodies; invent an electroscope, differentiate between static electricity and magnetism, conceive of the earth as a magnet. Written by the first great experimental scientist, this lively work is valuable not only as an historical landmark, but as the delightfully easy to follow record of a perpetually searching, ingenious mind. Translated by P. F. Mottelay. 25-page biographical memoir. 90 figures. lix +368pp. 5⅜ x 8.   S470 Paperbound **$2.00**

ASTRONOMY

THE INTERNAL CONSTITUTION OF THE STARS, Sir A. S. Eddington. Influence of this has been enormous; first detailed exposition of theory of radiative equilibrium for stellar interiors, of all available evidence for existence of diffuse matter in interstellar space. Studies quantum theory, polytropic gas spheres, mass-luminosity relations, variable stars, etc. Discussions of equations paralleled with informal exposition of intimate relationship of astrophysics with great discoveries in atomic physics, radiation. Introduction. Appendix. Index. 421pp. 5⅜ x 8.
S563 Paperbound **$2.25**

PLANETARY THEORY, E. W. Brown and C. A. Shook. Provides a clear presentation of basic methods for calculating planetary orbits for today's astronomer. Begins with a careful exposition of specialized mathematical topics essential for handling perturbation theory and then goes on to indicate how most of the previous methods reduce ultimately to two general calculation methods: obtaining expressions either for the coordinates of planetary positions or for the elements which determine the perturbed paths. An example of each is given and worked in detail. Corrected edition. Preface. Appendix. Index. xii + 302pp. 5⅜ x 8½.
S1133 Paperbound **$2.25**

CANON OF ECLIPSES (CANON DER FINSTERNISSE), Prof. Theodor Ritter von Oppolzer. Since its original publication in 1887, this has been the standard reference and the most extensive single volume of data on the calculation of solar and lunar eclipses, past and future. A comprehensive introduction gives a full explanation of the use of the tables for the calculations of the exact dates of eclipses, etc. Data furnished for the calculation of 8,000 solar and 5,200 lunar eclipses, going back as far as 1200 B.C. and giving predictions up to the year 2161. Information is also given for partial and ring eclipses. All calculations based on Universal (Greenwich) Time. An unsurpassed reference work for astronomers, scientists engaged in space research and developments, historians, etc. Unabridged republication, with corrections. Preface to this edition by Donald Menzel and Owen Gingerich of the Harvard College Observatory. Translated by Owen Gingerich. 160 charts. lxx + 538pp. 8⅜ x 11¼.
S114 Clothbound **$10.00**

THEORY OF THE MOTION OF THE HEAVENLY BODIES MOVING ABOUT THE SUN IN CONIC SECTIONS, Karl Friedrich Gauss. A landmark of theoretical astronomy by the great German scientist. Still authoritative and invaluable to the practicing astronomer. Part I develops the relations between the quantities on which the motion about the sun of the heavenly bodies depends—relations pertaining simply to position in the orbit, simply to position in space, between several places in orbit, and between several places in space. The calculation methods of Part II based on the groundwork of Part I include: determination of an orbit from 3 complete observations, from 4 observations (of which only two are complete), determination of an orbit satisfying as nearly as possible any number of observations whatever, and determination of orbits, taking into account the perturbations. Translation of "Theoria Motus" and with an appendix by C. H. Davis. Unabridged republication. Appendices and tables. 13 figures. xviii + 376pp. 6½ x 9¼.   S1056 Paperbound **$2.95**

THE GALACTIC NOVAE, C. Payne-Gaposchkin, Prof. of Astronomy, Harvard Univ. A work that will be the standard reference source for years to come. Gathers together all the pertinent data, results recorded by countless observers of galactic novae over the centuries, in order to formulate a valid starting point for an interpretation of the nova process. Covers information and statistics on known novae, their variations in luminosity, distribution in the sky, spectral changes, etc.; symbiotic novae; frequently-recurring variables of the U Geminorum and Z Camelopardis class; supernovae; comparison of spectral changes; theories and interpretations of these phenomena, etc. "A comprehensive summary of everything that is now known about these stars," SCIENCE. Bibliographical references. Preface. Indices. 49 figures. 6 plates. 101 tables. x + 336pp. 5⅜ x 8⅜. S1170 Paperbound **$2.45**

BINARY STARS, R. G. Aitken. Still the definitive work in the field of double star astronomy. Written by the director of the Lick Observatory (considered the father of the modern study of binary star systems), this book sums up the results of 40 years of experience in the field, plus the work of centuries of research. Includes historical survey of major discoveries and contributions of the past, observational methods for visual binary stars, the radial velocity of a star (by Dr. J. H. Moore), eclipsing binary stars, known orbits of binary stars, some binary systems of special interest, the origin of binary stars. Much information on methods of spectrum analysis, orbit plotting, use of the telescope, and other practical matters. Useful for classroom study and advanced hobbyists, etc. Revised edition, corrected and with additional notes by Prof. J. T. Kent. New preface. 50 tables, 13 figures, 4 full-page plates. Bibliographies. Appendix. Indices. xii + 309pp. 5⅜ x 8½. S1102 Paperbound **$2.00**

THE NATURE OF COMETS, N. B. Richter. An authority on comets presents a concise, but thorough survey of the state of our present-day knowledge of comets and cometary activity. Based on over 20 years of research, this is a middle-level account that even the layman can appreciate, providing a fund of information on historical theories (from 1700 to the present); statistical research on total number of comets, orbital forms, perturbations caused by Jupiter, comet groups, etc.; the structure of a comet; comets as processes of cosmic decay; origin and formation of comets; etc. Also: a lengthy introduction on modern theories by Dr. R. A. Lyttleton, much technical data and observational material of specific comets, supplementary tables, and the like. Revised (1963) edition. Translated and revised by Arthur Beer. 69 illustrations, including 54 photographs of comets, tails, spectra. 41 tables. Bibliography. Index. xli + 221pp. S1111 Clothbound **$10.00**

CELESTIAL OBJECTS FOR COMMON TELESCOPES, Rev. T. W. Webb. Classic handbook for the use and pleasure of the amateur astronomer. Of inestimable aid in locating and identifying thousands of celestial objects. Vol. I, The Solar System: discussions of the principle and operation of the telescope, procedures of observations and telescope-photography, spectroscopy, etc., precise location information of sun, moon, planets, meteors. Vol. II, The Stars: alphabetical listing of constellations, information on double stars, clusters, stars with unusual spectra, variables, and nebulae, etc. Nearly 4,000 objects noted. Edited and extensively revised by Margaret W. Mayall, director of the American Assn. of Variable Star Observers. New Index by Mrs. Mayall giving the location of all objects mentioned in the text for Epoch 2000. New Precession Table added. New appendices on the planetary satellites, constellation names and abbreviations, and solar system data. Total of 46 illustrations. Total of xxxix + 606pp. 5⅜ x 8. Vol. I: T917 Paperbound **$2.25**
Vol. II: T918 Paperbound **$2.25**
Two Volume Set Paperbound **$4.50**

ASTRONOMY AND COSMOGONY, Sir James Jeans. A modern classic which is still of enormous value to everyone in astronomy, etc., this is Jean's last and most famous exposition. The summation of a lifetime's devotion to science, it presents his final conclusions on a host of problems ranging over the whole of descriptive astronomy, astrophysics, stellar dynamics, and cosmology. Contents: The Light from the Stars, Gaseous Stars, the Source of Stellar Energy, Liquid Stars, The Evolution of the Stars, The Configuration of Rotating Masses, The Evolution of Binary Systems, The Ages of the Stars, The Great Nebulae, The Galactic Systems, Variable Stars, etc. New preface by L. Motz, Columbia U. 16 full-page photographic illustrations. xv + 428pp. 5⅝ x 8⅜. S923 Paperbound **$2.45**

ASTRONOMY OF STELLAR ENERGY AND DECAY, Martin Johnson. Middle level treatment of astronomy as interpreted by modern atomic physics. Part One is non-technical, examines physical properties, source of energy, spectroscopy, fluctuating stars, various models and theories, etc. Part Two parallels these topics, providing their mathematical foundation. "Clear, concise, and readily understandable," American Library Assoc. Bibliography. 3 indexes. 29 illustrations. 216pp. 5⅜ x 8. S537 Paperbound **$1.50**

MATHEMATICAL THEORIES OF PLANETARY MOTIONS, Otto Dziobek. Translated by Mark W. Harrington and William J. Hussey. Lucid account of the principles of mathematical astronomy. It examines that part of celestial mechanics which deals with the motions of heavenly bodies considered as material points. Contents: Solution of the Problem of Two Bodies; Formation of the General Integrals for Problem of n Bodies . . . including discussions of elliptic, parabolic, and hyperbolic orbits, the solution of Kepler's equation, etc.; and sections headed The General Properties of the Integrals and The Theory of Perturbations . . . which deals with the theory of absolute perturbations, analytical development of the perturbing function, the variation of the elements, the secular variation of the mean longitude, etc. vi + 294pp. 5⅜ x 8½. S129 Paperbound **$2.00**

A COMPENDIUM OF SPHERICAL ASTRONOMY, S. Newcomb. Long a standard collection of basic methods and formulas most useful to the working astronomer, and clear full text for students. Includes the most important common approximations; 40 pages on the method of least squares; general theory of spherical coordinates; parallax; aberration; astronomical refraction; theory of precession; proper motion of the stars; methods of deriving positions of stars; and much more. Index. 9 Appendices of tables, formulas, etc. 36 figures. xviii + 444pp. 5⅜ x 8.

S690 Paperbound **$2.25**

PRINCIPLES OF STELLAR DYNAMICS, S. Chandrasekhar. A leading astrophysicist here presents the theory of stellar dynamics as a branch of classical dynamics, clarifying the fundamental issues and the underlying motivations of the theory. He analyzes the effects of stellar encounters in terms of the classical 2-body problem, and investigates problems centering about Liouville's theorem and the solutions of the equations of continuity. This edition also includes 4 important papers by the author published since "Stellar Dynamics," and equally indispensable for all workers in the field: "New Methods in Stellar Dynamics" and "Dynamical Friction," Parts I, II, and III. Index. 3 Appendixes. Bibliography. 50 illustrations. x + 313pp. 5⅜ x8.

S659 Paperbound **$2.00**

AN INTRODUCTION TO THE STUDY OF STELLAR STRUCTURE, Subrahmanyan Chandrasekhar. Outstanding treatise on stellar dynamics by one of world's greatest astrophysicists. Uses classical & modern math methods to examine relationship between loss of energy, the mass, and radius of stars in a steady state. Discusses thermodynamic laws from Carathéodory's axiomatic standpoint; adiabatic, polytropic laws; work of Ritter, Emden, Kelvin, others; Stroemgren envelopes as starter for theory of gaseous stars; Gibbs statistical mechanics (quantum); degenerate stellar configuration & theory of white dwarfs, etc. "Highest level of scientific merit," BULLETIN, AMER. MATH. SOC. Bibliography. Appendixes. Index. 33 figures. 509pp. 5⅜ x 8.

S413 Paperbound **$2.75**

STATISTICAL ASTRONOMY, Robert J. Trumpler and Harold F. Weaver, University of California. Standard introduction to the principles and techniques of statistical astronomy, a field of rapidly growing importance in this space age. An extensive section, "Elements of Statistical Theory," provides the astronomer with the tools for solving problems of descriptive astronomy, observational errors, constitution of extra-galactic nebulae, etc. Procedures used in statistical astronomy are related to basic mathematical principles of statistics such as unvariate distribution, integral equations, general theory of samples, etc. Other sections deal with: Statistical Description of the Galactic System; Stellar Motions in the Vicinity of the Sun; Luminosity—Spectral Type Distribution; Space Distribution of Stars; and Galactic Rotation. List of symbols. Appendix (10 tables). 2 Indexes. Extensive bibliography. 31 tables. 97 figures. xxi + 644pp. 5⅜ x 8½.

S301 Paperbound **$3.00**

AN INTRODUCTORY TREATISE ON DYNAMICAL ASTRONOMY, H. C. Plummer. Unusually wide connected and concise coverage of nearly every significant branch of dynamical astronomy, stressing basic principles throughout: determination of orbits, planetary theory, lunar theory, precession and nutation, and many of their applications. Hundreds of formulas and theorems worked out completely, important methods thoroughly explained. Covers motion under a central attraction, orbits of double stars and spectroscopic binaries, the libration of the moon, and much more. Index. 8 diagrams. xxi + 343pp. 5⅜ x 8⅜.

S689 Paperbound **$2.35**

AN INTRODUCTORY TREATISE ON THE LUNAR THEORY, E. W. Brown. Indispensable for all scientists and engineers interested in orbital calculation, satellites, or navigation of space. Only work in English to explain in detail 5 major mathematical approaches to the problem of 3 bodies, those of Laplace, de Pontécoulant, Hansen, Delaunay, and Hill. Covers expressions for mutual attraction, equations of motion, forms of solution, variations of the elements in disturbed motion, the constants and their interpretations, planetary and other disturbing influences, etc. Index. Bibliography. Tables. xvi + 292pp. 5⅝ x 8⅜.

S666 Paperbound **$2.00**

SPHERICAL AND PRACTICAL ASTRONOMY, W. Chauvenet. First book in English to apply mathematical techniques to astronomical problems is still standard work. Covers almost entire field, rigorously, with over 300 examples worked out. Vol. 1, spherical astronomy, applications to nautical astronomy; determination of hour angles, parallactic angle for known stars; interpolation; parallax; laws of refraction; predicting eclipses; precession, nutation of fixed stars; etc. Vol. 2, theory, use, of instruments; telescope; measurement of arcs, angles in general; electro-chronograph; sextant, reflecting circles; zenith telescope; etc. 100-page appendix of detailed proof of Gauss' method of least squares. 5th revised edition. Index. 15 plates, 20 tables. 1340pp. 5⅜ x 8.

Vol. 1 S618 Paperbound **$2.75**
Vol. 2 S619 Paperbound **$2.75**
The set **$5.50**

RADIATIVE TRANSFER, S. Chandrasekhar. Definitive work in field provides foundation for analysis of stellar atmospheres, planetary illumination, sky radiation; to physicists, a study of problems analogous to those in theory of diffusion of neutrons. Partial contents: equation of transfer, isotropic scattering, H-functions, diffuse reflection and transmission, Rayleigh scattering, X, Y functions, radiative equilibrium of stellar atmospheres. Extensive bibliography. 3 appendices. 35 tables. 35 figures. 407pp. 5⅝ x 8⅜.

S599 Paperbound **$2.25**

GEOLOGY, GEOGRAPHY, METEOROLOGY

PRINCIPLES OF STRATIGRAPHY, A. W. Grabau. Classic of 20th century geology, unmatched in scope and comprehensiveness. Nearly 600 pages cover the structure and origins of every kind of sedimentary, hydrogenic, oceanic, pyroclastic, atmoclastic, hydroclastic, marine hydroclastic, and bioclastic rock; metamorphism; erosion; etc. Includes also the constitution of the atmosphere; morphology of oceans, rivers, glaciers; volcanic activities; faults and earthquakes; and fundamental principles of paleontology (nearly 200 pages). New introduction by Prof. M. Kay, Columbia U. 1277 bibliographical entries. 264 diagrams. Tables, maps, etc. Two volume set. Total of xxxii + 1185pp. 5⅜ x 8.
S686 Vol I Paperbound **$2.50**
S687 Vol II Paperbound **$2.50**
The set **$5.00**

TREATISE ON SEDIMENTATION, William H. Twenhofel. A milestone in the history of geology, this two-volume work, prepared under the auspices of the United States Research Council, contains practically everything known about sedimentation up to 1932. Brings together all the findings of leading American and foreign geologists and geographers and has never been surpassed for completeness, thoroughness of description, or accuracy of detail. Vol. 1 discusses the sources and production of sediments, their transportation, deposition, diagenesis, and lithification. Also modification of sediments by organisms and topographical, climatic, etc. conditions which contribute to the alteration of sedimentary processes. 220 pages deal with products of sedimentation: minerals, limestones, dolomites, coals, etc. Vol. 2 continues the examination of products such as gypsum and saline residues, silica, strontium, manganese, etc. An extensive exposition of structures, textures and colors of sediments: stratification, cross-lamination, ripple mark, oolitic and pisolitic textures, etc. Chapters on environments or realms of sedimentation and field and laboratory techniques are also included. Indispensable to modern-day geologists and students. Index. List of authors cited. 1733-item bibliography. 121 diagrams. Total of xxxiii + 926pp. 5⅜ x 8½.
Vol. I: S950 Paperbound **$2.50**
Vol. II: S951 Paperbound **$2.50**
Two volume set Paperbound **$5.00**

THE EVOLUTION OF THE IGNEOUS ROCKS, N. L. Bowen. Invaluable serious introduction applies techniques of physics and chemistry to explain igneous rock diversity in terms of chemical composition and fractional crystallization. Discusses liquid immiscibility in silicate magmas, crystal sorting, liquid lines of descent, fractional resorption of complex minerals, petrogenesis, etc. Of prime importance to geologists & mining engineers, also to physicists, chemists working with high temperatures and pressures. "Most important," TIMES, London. 3 indexes. 263 bibliographic notes. 82 figures. xviii + 334pp. 5⅜ x 8.
S311 Paperbound **$2.00**

INTERNAL CONSTITUTION OF THE EARTH, edited by Beno Gutenberg. Completely revised. Brought up-to-date, reset. Prepared for the National Research Council this is a complete & thorough coverage of such topics as earth origins, continent formation, nature & behavior of the earth's core, petrology of the crust, cooling forces in the core, seismic & earthquake material, gravity, elastic constants, strain characteristics and similar topics. "One is filled with admiration . . . a high standard . . . there is no reader who will not learn something from this book," London, Edinburgh, Dublin, Philosophic Magazine. Largest bibliography in print: 1127 classified items. Indexes. Tables of constants. 43 diagrams. 439pp. 6⅛ x 9¼.
S414 Paperbound **$3.00**

HYDROLOGY, edited by Oscar E. Meinzer. Prepared for the National Research Council. Detailed complete reference library on precipitation, evaporation, snow, snow surveying, glaciers, lakes, infiltration, soil moisture, ground water, runoff, drought, physical changes produced by water, hydrology of limestone terranes, etc. Practical in application, especially valuable for engineers. 24 experts have created "the most up-to-date, most complete treatment of the subject," AM. ASSOC. of PETROLEUM GEOLOGISTS. Bibliography. Index. 165 illustrations. xi + 712pp. 6⅛ x 9¼.
S191 Paperbound **$3.25**

SNOW CRYSTALS, W. A. Bentley and W. J. Humphreys. Over 200 pages of Bentley's famous microphotographs of snow flakes—the product of painstaking, methodical work at his Jericho, Vermont studio. The pictures, which also include plates of frost, glaze and dew on vegetation, spider webs, windowpanes; sleet; graupel or soft hail, were chosen both for their scientific interest and their aesthetic qualities. The wonder of nature's diversity is exhibited in the intricate, beautiful patterns of the snow flakes. Introductory text by W. J. Humphreys. Selected bibliography. 2,453 illustrations. 224pp. 8 x 10¼.
T287 Paperbound **$2.95**

PHYSICS OF THE AIR, W. J. Humphreys. A very thorough coverage of classical materials and theories in meteorology . . . written by one of this century's most highly respected physical meteorologists. Contains the standard account in English of atmospheric optics. 5 main sections: Mechanics and Thermodynamics of the Atmosphere, Atmospheric Electricity and Auroras, Meteorological Acoustics, Atmospheric Optics, and Factors of Climatic Control. Under these headings, topics covered are: theoretical relations between temperature, pressure, and volume in the atmosphere; composition, pressure, and density; circulation; evaporation and condensation; fog, clouds, thunderstorms; lightning; aurora polaris; principal ice-age theories; etc. New preface by Prof. Julius London. 226 illustrations. Index. xviii + 676pp. 5⅜ x 8½.
S1044 Paperbound **$3.00**

CHEMISTRY AND PHYSICAL CHEMISTRY

ORGANIC CHEMISTRY, F. C. Whitmore. The entire subject of organic chemistry for the practicing chemist and the advanced student. Storehouse of facts, theories, processes found elsewhere only in specialized journals. Covers aliphatic compounds (500 pages on the properties and synthetic preparation of hydrocarbons, halides, proteins, ketones, etc.), alicyclic compounds, aromatic compounds, heterocyclic compounds, organophosphorus and organometallic compounds. Methods of synthetic preparation analyzed critically throughout. Includes much of biochemical interest. "The scope of this volume is astonishing," INDUSTRIAL AND ENGINEERING CHEMISTRY. 12,000-reference index. 2387-item bibliography. Total of x + 1005pp. 5⅜ x 8. Two volume set.
S700 Vol I Paperbound **$2.00**
S701 Vol II Paperbound **$2.00**
The set **$4.00**

THE MODERN THEORY OF MOLECULAR STRUCTURE, Bernard Pullman. A reasonably popular account of recent developments in atomic and molecular theory. Contents: The Wave Function and Wave Equations (history and bases of present theories of molecular structure); The Electronic Structure of Atoms (Description and classification of atomic wave functions, etc.); Diatomic Molecules; Non-Conjugated Polyatomic Molecules; Conjugated Polyatomic Molecules; The Structure of Complexes. Minimum of mathematical background needed. New translation by David Antin of "La Structure Moleculaire." Index. Bibliography. vii + 87pp. 5⅜ x 8½.
S987 Paperbound **$1.00**

CATALYSIS AND CATALYSTS, Marcel Prettre, Director, Research Institute on Catalysis. This brief book, translated into English for the first time, is the finest summary of the principal modern concepts, methods, and results of catalysis. Ideal introduction for beginning chemistry and physics students. Chapters: Basic Definitions of Catalysis (true catalysis and generalization of the concept of catalysis); The Scientific Bases of Catalysis (Catalysis and chemical thermodynamics, catalysis and chemical kinetics); Homogeneous Catalysis (acid-base catalysis, etc.); Chain Reactions; Contact Masses; Heterogeneous Catalysis (Mechanisms of contact catalyses, etc.); and Industrial Applications (acids and fertilizers, petroleum and petroleum chemistry, rubber, plastics, synthetic resins, and fibers). Translated by David Antin. Index. vi + 88pp. 5⅜ x 8½.
S998 Paperbound **$1.00**

POLAR MOLECULES, Pieter Debye. This work by Nobel laureate Debye offers a complete guide to fundamental electrostatic field relations, polarizability, molecular structure. Partial contents: electric intensity, displacement and force, polarization by orientation, molar polarization and molar refraction, halogen-hydrides, polar liquids, ionic saturation, dielectric constant, etc. Special chapter considers quantum theory. Indexed. 172pp. 5⅜ x 8.
S64 Paperbound **$1.50**

THE ELECTRONIC THEORY OF ACIDS AND BASES, W. F. Luder and Saverio Zuffanti. The first full systematic presentation of the electronic theory of acids and bases—treating the theory and its ramifications in an uncomplicated manner. Chapters: Historical Background; Atomic Orbitals and Valence; The Electronic Theory of Acids and Bases; Electrophilic and Electrodotic Reagents; Acidic and Basic Radicals; Neutralization; Titrations with Indicators; Displacement; Catalysis; Acid Catalysis; Base Catalysis; Alkoxides and Catalysts; Conclusion. Required reading for all chemists. Second revised (1961) eidtion, with additional examples and references. 3 figures. 9 tables. Index. Bibliography xii + 165pp. 5⅜ x 8.
S201 Paperbound **$1.50**

KINETIC THEORY OF LIQUIDS, J. Frenkel. Regarding the kinetic theory of liquids as a generalization and extension of the theory of solid bodies, this volume covers all types of arrangements of solids, thermal displacements of atoms, interstitial atoms and ions, orientational and rotational motion of molecules, and transition between states of matter. Mathematical theory is developed close to the physical subject matter. 216 bibliographical footnotes. 55 figures. xi + 485pp. 5⅜ x 8.
S95 Paperbound **$2.55**

THE PRINCIPLES OF ELECTROCHEMISTRY, D. A. MacInnes. Basic equations for almost every subfield of electrochemistry from first principles, referring at all times to the soundest and most recent theories and results; unusually useful as text or as reference. Covers coulometers and Faraday's Law, electrolytic conductance, the Debye-Hueckel method for the theoretical calculation of activity coefficients, concentration cells, standard electrode potentials, thermodynamic ionization constants, pH, potentiometric titrations, irreversible phenomena, Planck's equation, and much more. "Excellent treatise," AMERICAN CHEMICAL SOCIETY JOURNAL. "Highly recommended," CHEMICAL AND METALLURGICAL ENGINEERING. 2 Indices. Appendix. 585-item bibliography. 137 figures. 94 tables. ii + 478pp. 5⅝ x 8⅜.
S52 Paperbound **$2.45**

THE PHASE RULE AND ITS APPLICATION, Alexander Findlay. Covering chemical phenomena of 1, 2, 3, 4, and multiple component systems, this "standard work on the subject" (NATURE, London), has been completely revised and brought up to date by A. N. Campbell and N. O. Smith. Brand new material has been added on such matters as binary, tertiary liquid equilibria, solid solutions in ternary systems, quinary systems of salts and water. Completely revised to triangular coordinates in ternary systems, clarified graphic representation, solid models, etc. 9th revised edition. Author, subject indexes. 236 figures. 505 footnotes, mostly bibliographic. xii + 494pp. 5⅜ x 8.
S91 Paperbound **$2.45**

THE SOLUBILITY OF NONELECTROLYTES, Joel H. Hildebrand and Robert L. Scott. The standard work on the subject; still indispensable as a reference source and for classroom work. Partial contents: The Ideal Solution (including Raoult's Law and Henry's Law, etc.); Nonideal Solutions; Intermolecular Forces; The Liquid State; Entropy of Athermal Mixing; Heat of Mixing; Polarity; Hydrogen Bonding; Specific Interactions; "Solvation" and "Association"; Systems of Three or More Components; Vapor Pressure of Binary Liquid Solutions; Mixtures of Gases; Solubility of Gases in Liquids; of Liquids in Liquids; of Solids in Liquids; Evaluation of Solubility Parameters; and other topics. Corrected republication of third (revised) edition. Appendices. Indexes. 138 figures. 111 tables. 1 photograph. iv + 488pp. 5⅜ x 8½.
S1125 Paperbound $2.50

TERNARY S **YSTEMS, G. Masing.** Fu **mechanical** in solid m **tion series;** mixture wi **num alloys;** solid soluti **166 illustra-** allotropic **pound $1.50** tions. 178pp

THE KINETI **mprehensive** text and re **important** experiments **Partial con-** tents: The **Deductions,** Distribution **of specific** heats, the **magnetic** properties o **gases.** New 14-page pre **appendices.** 570-item bib **pound $2.95**

IONS IN SO **overing all** the fundamer **wn author-** ity. Contains **ce energy,** transferral of **exchange** forces, hydr **d topics.** Indispensable **try.** Index. 45 illustration **pound $1.50**

IONIC PROCE **tion which** brings togeth **mechanics,** electroacousti **n of the** behavior of i **extensive** and technical **level text** for graduate s **Brownian** motion in liq **solution,** proton transfe **ions, etc.** 78 illustration **und $1.75**

CRYSTALLOGRA **aylor and** B. J. Kagle, W **crystallo-** graphic data o **ssed uni-** formly in abso **data from** the Power Dat **ables, as** well as from **rst table,** Alloys and Inte **stings for** nearly 700 Bo **data on** the crystal stru **nd $2.25**

MATHEMATICAL **Harold** Hilton. Classic **the geo-** metrical theory **Federow,** Schoenflies, and **Common** to Symmetrical **quivalent** Points, Crystall **Lattices** and Translations **d Mono-** clinic Groups, O **d $2.00**

CLASSICS IN TH **Vol. I of** the Classics of **his book** is a collection o **valence** concept in chem **rankland,** Kekulé and Coup **nsion of** the valence con **ogue by** Prof. Benfey. In **xiv +** 191pp. 5⅜ x 8 **Paperbound $1.85**

DATE DUE

OCT 0 1 1992

NOV 2 1 1996

GAYLORD

PRINTED IN U.S.A.